THE WORLD OF THE COYOTE

A LIVING WORLD BOOK
John K. Terres, Editor

LIVING WORLD BOOKS
John K. Terres, Editor

The World of the

Coyote

Text and Photographs by

Joe Van Wormer

J. B. LIPPINCOTT COMPANY

Philadelphia & New York

Grateful acknowledgment is made to *Audubon Magazine* for permission to quote from the article "Coyotes Protected" by E. C. Shindorf, which appeared in the September-October, 1953, issue.

To Helen, Sunny, and Jill
for Their Patience and Encouragement

Contents

The World of the Coyote

Meet the Coyote

COYOTES BELONG to the world-wide family Canidae, which includes dogs, wolves, jackals, and foxes.* Like the rest of the family, coyotes have long narrow muzzles, erect ears, slender limbs, and bushy tails. Their body temperature is regulated by panting, with moisture being passed off through the tongue. Sensitive ears, sharp eyes, and a keen sense of smell are common characteristics. Along with bears and raccoons, they evolved from the Miacidae, a family of small, tree-climbing carnivorous mammals that lived 50 million years ago.

It is interesting to note that the most domesticated of all animals, the dog, is blood brother to what is probably the cleverest of all wild animals found in the United States, the coyote.

The coyote (*Canis latrans*) is actually a small wolf, the smallest in North America. On the average it is about half as large as the near-extinct red wolf (*Canis niger*) and about one-third the size of the scarce gray or timber wolf (*Canis lupus*). It resembles a medium-sized dog of the collie-shepherd type, though its nose is narrower and pointed like a fox's. The coyote's legs are thinner than those of most dogs and its feet are smaller than a dog of equal body size. Its large pointed ears, facing forward, are movable and can be directed in order to catch sound vibrations. The coyote's eyes are round, the iris yellow.

---

* Members of the dog family are social, and may hunt in packs, running down their prey by sheer speed and endurance. Their legs are adapted for running, and they seize their prey in their mouths rather than with their claws, as members of the cat family do.—EDITOR.

13

Coyote and dog—brothers under the skin.

The sharp, piercing eyes of the coyote never miss a thing.

Meet the Coyote

Like the dog's, the coyote's cylindrically shaped bushy tail is an accurate barometer of his mental state. When pleased, he wags it; when frightened, he tucks it between his legs.

The coloration of a mature coyote is basically light buff-gray. The muzzle and ears are strongly accented rust and fulvous, and the same color tones, to a lesser degree, are present on the outside of both front and hind legs. The intensity and amount of this coloring vary considerably between specimens. The upper lip and under parts are whitish. Most of the upper parts of the animal are sprinkled with long black-tipped hairs which add strong accents of black to the pelt, depending upon the angle from which it is viewed. This coloration carries forward into the tail, which usually is tipped with black. However, I have seen coyotes without black hair on their tails. On others the tip is not markedly black, and on an occasional specimen the tip of the tail is pure white.

As with other mammals, notably the bobcat, altitude and habitat are factors in coyote coloration. Those that live in higher elevations

This coyote has a normal black-tipped tail.

and heavily timbered areas tend to be darker colored, with stronger black accents. Those from lower altitudes and open desert areas are more fulvous and tend to be light gray. In both, the coloration is one which blends protectively with the habitat.

The coyote, like other members of the dog family, has a scent gland with a definite individual scent. Situated on the upper side of the tail near the base, it provides individual identification when coyotes meet. Identification by smell, similar to that which everyone has observed among dogs, takes place. These glands, along with coyote urine, have long been used by trappers for ingredients of their scent lures.

A coyote weighs between 20 and 50 pounds at maturity, with the average being 22 to 25 pounds. The heaviest coyote on record, insofar as I've been able to determine, was a male killed in Wyoming in 1937 that weighed 74.8 pounds. Other large specimens include a 53.3-pound male from Michigan and a 42-pound male from South Dakota. Males average slightly heavier than females: 446 males from New Mexico averaged 24.4 pounds, and 383 females from the same state averaged 22.2 pounds. There is some indication that mountain coyotes are heavier than those of the lowlands.

The coyote stands about 2 feet high at the shoulders. Its body, including a tail length of 11 to 16 inches, is about 4 feet long. Coyotes do not hibernate, nor do they have a period of inactivity or dormancy during the winter.

Thomas Say, an early American zoologist, first gave a specific name to the coyote after becoming acquainted with the animal while he was the naturalist on Army engineer Stephen H. Long's expedition to the Rocky Mountains in 1820. Say gave this noisy wild dog of the western prairies the scientific name *Canis latrans,* which means "barking dog."

Early Anglo-American observers appropriately called the coyote a "prairie wolf," as it spends most of its time in open or brushy country, as distinguished from the timber wolf, which includes heavy forests in its habitat. Other names that were given it were "brush wolf,"

17

The tail of this animal is without the customary black tip. Body color carries right on through to the very end of the tail.

The World of the Coyote

"barking wolf," "American jackal," "heul wolf," "steppen wolf," and "cased wolf." This latter name came from the way trappers removed the pelt from a coyote. The pelt of the larger gray wolf was slit down the belly and then stretched out flat to dry. With the coyote, or "cased wolf," the skin was peeled off without slitting (like taking off a glove by turning it wrong side out) and then dried over a frame.

In time, these names were dropped in favor of "coyote" (pronounced "kie'oat," or "kie-oh'tee") which comes from the Spanish and is a modification of the Aztec word *coyotl.*

Coyotes apparently were important to the Aztecs and figured prominently in their religious activities, as indicated by coyote symbols and

This is typical of much of the coyote's homeland—semi-open, and brush-covered. For this reason the animal was often known as a "brush wolf."

representative carvings found in Aztec ruins. Obviously, the Indian mind was somewhat in awe of the coyote and its capabilities and made the animal the basis for many legends and superstitions.

To these can be added the white man's tall tales about coyotes and their prowess which, in total, forms an amazing amount of literature (both oral and written) about coyotes and their miraculous powers. Ella E. Clark's *Indian Legends of the Pacific Northwest* (University of California Press, 1953) contains the following legends which are indicative of the early Indians' general feelings toward the coyote: "How Coyote Made the Columbia River," "Coyote and the Monster of the Columbia," "How Coyote Changed the Course of the Columbia

A coyote hunting in open desert country.

River," "How Coyote Helped the People," "How Coyote Made the Indian Tribes," "How Coyote Brought Fire to the People," and "Coyote and Eagle Visit the Land of the Dead."

It is obvious from these titles that the Indians considered the coyote to be extremely powerful.

Early Indian medicine men claimed they could interpret the yelpings of coyotes to determine if friend or enemy were approaching. The white men who moved west also put considerable faith in the coyotes' howl, but for more practical reasons. They learned that when the wily little brush wolf was around, hostile Indians were not likely to be skulking through the sage and, conversely, when the prairies were quiet and the song of the coyote was missing, it was time to double the guards and be alert.

The name "coyote" has worked its way into our language in considerable depth and there's hardly a locality in the West that doesn't have a "Coyote Hills," "Coyote Springs" or some other landmark or geographical feature named after the animal. Real or fancied coyote characteristics are applied to people by using the word "coyote" as an adjective or verb. For example: "coyoting around" is a derogatory term meaning mooching or begging, while to "out-coyote" someone is complimentary and means to outsmart him. People can be "coyote mean" or "coyote smart." It seems that most of these sayings are, in some way, a compliment to the intelligence and abilities of the coyote.

Back-country Mexicans have a game with "chickens" on one side and "coyotes" on the other. I do not know if the games are the same but the name reminds me of "fox and geese" played by youngsters in the United States.

Temporary shelters erected by some early settlers—notably the Mormons in Great Salt Valley, Utah—were called coyote houses. They were nothing more than dirt cellars dug in the ground which were roofed over with a few boards and thus resembled the den of a coyote.

The present range of the coyote extends from Point Barrow, Alaska,

to tropical Costa Rica in Central America, a distance of about 7,500 miles. The western border is the Pacific Ocean and, in recent times, the animal has spread into the eastern United States and the south-eastern part of Canada. However, when early explorers first went west, the coyote's range appears to have been confined to areas west of the Mississippi and from southern Canada to central Mexico.

The coyote is primarily an animal of the open plains and desert. This preference was, I think, based mostly on availability of food. Deer, elk, and antelope were, at first, open-range animals. It was hunting pressure from man that forced deer and elk to take refuge in timbered sections. Furthermore, the vast timbered areas of the West

21

were, in many places, so dense that the ground was in perpetual twilight. The brush cover that would have provided food and shelter for rodents did not grow there.

There is a section of beautiful ponderosa pine timber in the part of central Oregon where I live that twenty years ago looked like a well-groomed city park. No brushy growth marred its smooth carpet of needles. A friend who had known the country many years before I did stated that thirty years before I saw it, most of that section looked the same and there were few if any deer there. Since then, of course, logging operations have opened some sections and thinned others.

Western coyote country—open, dry and big.

With the forest floor opened to sunlight the forest understory has regrown and small animals flourish. Deer have become so plentiful that special seasons have been held to thin out their numbers and prevent their ultimate starvation from overbrowsing. And, of course, the coyote followed its food supply and moved into the forest from the open desert a dozen miles away.

As man and his livestock moved westward, a new source of food became available to coyotes. Timber was cut and livestock moved about and the coyote found its habits changing as it followed this

23

source of easily obtainable food. Great herds of sheep were moved from lowland pastures up through the timbered slopes of the mountain ranges to the lush high mountain meadows for summer grazing. Coyotes followed and inhabited new country.

The coyote's movement southward into Central America can be attributed to livestock brought in by Spaniards in the sixteenth century. Coyotes moved south as livestock moved south.

Though it happened 300 years later, it is believed that the coyote migration into northern British Columbia, the Yukon Territory, and, finally, into Alaska was for the same reason.

24

Meet the Coyote

This successful encroachment by the coyote on an area where the northern timber wolf is still plentiful is a remarkable tribute to the coyote's ability to survive. In the cold vastness of the North, food supplies are often meager and competition for food is keen. It is quite likely that the coyote's catholic appetite and its adaptability to man's presence allow it to compete with the wolves' greater size and strength. According to Ernest Thompson Seton and Stanley P. Young, wolves occasionally capture and kill coyotes.

The coyote first appeared in Alaska around 1915. There was a fast increase and spread of population which centered in the Tanana Valley around 1950. By 1953 this center had shifted to south-central Alaska. In February, 1964, the Alaska Department of Fish and Game reported: "We can advise that these animals are at an extremely low level of abundance in Alaska at this time. Formerly, we had good populations which apparently crashed as a result of rabies or some other disease."

Regardless of its movement into mountainous timbered sections and areas of much rain or snowfall in the North, the coyote is still mostly a flatland animal that seems to prefer its country dry. Despite the apparent contradiction of its movement into parts of the Northwest where there is also much rain and snowfall, the animal shuns wet tropical sections of its southern range. In Mexico and Central America it does not live in the tropical forested country on the eastern slopes nor in the eastern coastal prairies of Texas where tropical conditions also exist.

The movement of coyotes into the eastern United States appears to be partly natural, and partly a result of coyotes being brought by people from the West and released either accidentally or purposefully. Information received early in 1964 from the game commissions, or comparable departments, of the various states indicated that coyotes in the northeastern states are believed to have migrated into the area, while those in other eastern states are thought to have been im-

25

ported either by fox hunters, who thought they were getting foxes, or by returning western visitors who wanted to bring back exotic pets.

Also, early in 1964, these same state game commissions reported coyotes in all states east of the Mississippi, except Florida, Delaware, Kentucky, Maryland, North Carolina, South Carolina, Virginia, West Virginia, and Rhode Island.

Some of these reports were in conflict with supposedly authoritative information from other sources.

The Florida Game and Fresh Water Commission says: "Fox hunters on several occasions have imported coyotes but these do not seem to survive or reproduce."

An animal identified as a female coyote was taken in Kentucky on January 4, 1953, according to a report in *Journal of Mammalogy*. In February, 1964, I was advised by the Kentucky Department of Fish and Wildlife Resources as follows: "There was a coyote scare in Anderson and Woodford Counties along the Kentucky River which separates the two counties. This Department spent quite a bit of money in conjunction with the U. S. Fish and Wildlife Service in an effort to exterminate these animals. Several were trapped and taken to the University of Kentucky and Dr. Funkhouser, who is now deceased, declared all of them wild dogs. That was along about 1949 or 1950 and we haven't heard anything about coyotes since."

A coyote was reported killed in 1921 in Montgomery County, Maryland. However, in February, 1964, the Maryland Game and Inland Fish Commission reported no wild coyotes in that state.

The North Carolina Wildlife Resources Commission reported: ". . . to the best of our knowledge there is no record of any wild coyotes having been found in North Carolina."

From the South Carolina Wildlife Resources Commission came this statement: "There are, as far as we know, no coyotes in South Carolina. About a dozen years ago there were reports of some, and some dog-coyote crosses, but have heard nothing of these in some time. These animals, if they actually existed, were probably brought in as pets and escaped."

The Virginia Commission of Game and Inland Fisheries reported: "We have no record of coyotes being in the state for the past several years.

"There is no record showing official dates, but we do know that a coyote was killed in the western part of Virginia about ten years ago in connection with some sheep depredations. This animal was believed to have escaped captivity."

The West Virginia Department of Natural Resources advised: "There are no wild coyotes in this state at the present time. We have from time to time experienced wild coyotes from accidental or intentional releases. In all cases, the animals have been eliminated and present no problem at the present time."

The one state largely west of the Mississippi that seems to be without coyotes is Louisiana. Damp, near-sea-level terrain in combination with a warm climate do not seem suitable for coyotes. This possibility is also indicated by the report from Florida previously quoted.

In view of the extension of the coyote's range in the years since the white man came into its territory, one is inclined to speculate on how the coyote population of today would compare with that in the days before white settlers started their westward migration. The report from Alaska of a downward fluctuation of coyote numbers is an indication that certain natural forces tend to stabilize coyote populations.

Adolph Murie reported from his study of the coyote in Yellowstone Park: "In Yellowstone, after four years of absence of artificial control, it is apparent that coyotes have not multiplied according to mathematical expectations. The evidence shows that the population spread has been very limited and has been only in areas adjacent to the park boundaries . . . . There is no good way of measuring coyote abundance and we can make only rough estimates of the comparative sizes of populations from year to year. At any rate, coyote numbers seem to be remaining rather stable and not pyramiding."

The spread of the coyote since the coming of the white man to this continent is but an indication of the animal's amazing ability to adapt itself. It has done what few other mammals have been able to do in the face of advancing civilization—extended its range. Unlike many other species whose habitat requirements place limits on where they can live, the coyote has apparently responded to food supply rather than to limitations of climate and suitable range.

There are three sounds which epitomize all wildlife to me. These are the wild calls of the Canada goose as he heads south for the winter; the bugling challenge of the mighty bull elk during the rutting season; and the lonesome "song" of the coyote from a distant rimrock on a clear frosty night. The coyote's howl has a haunting quality that, once heard, is hard to forget.

It usually starts with a long, mournful, high-pitched howl and ends in a series of sharp yips and yaps. If, as frequently happens, other coyotes nearby join in the chorus, the resulting yip-yaps overlaying the prolonged howls, with the whole noisy ventriloqual mixture bounced back and forth from nearby hills and rimrocks, sound as if all the coyotes in the world have gathered together for singing lessons. Although this may be a slight exaggeration, the fact remains that a half-dozen coyotes howling together sound like a great many more.

One early fall morning I was slowly cruising through northeastern Yellowstone Park near Tower Falls. As I rounded a turn, I saw a full-grown coyote coming toward me. I stopped and the animal left the road and made its way unhurriedly down a hillside, through a creek bottom, and then crossed to a meadow on the other side. Here it stopped, turned its sharp nose to the clear morning sky and howled. Off to the right on a timbered hillside one answered; before it was through, a third answered from the opposite hill.

Meet the Coyote

A fourth coyote then came up through the meadow toward the first animal, acting, for all the world, like a playful puppy. I gathered from this and the comparative sizes of the two that the first was a female, the other one of her pups. This would have made it five or six months old at the time. After exchanging affectionate greetings, the two animals began to howl and yip and the other two joined in. Presently it sounded as if a dozen or more were sounding off. They kept it up intermittently for about five minutes and then stopped.

Coyotes seem to howl for all sorts of reasons. Some authorities suggest that they signal other coyotes, warn them of danger, and tell of feeding opportunities; that they ask for information and assistance. It

A coyote howling—one of the wildest sounds to be heard.

On a snowy winter's day in Yellowstone these five coyotes played together. They looked like young ones, ten months old, and were probably litter mates.

has also been said that they have at least three distinct calls: the *squeak*, the *howl call*, and a *distress call*.

While coyotes may communicate, I have never been able to distinguish messages in their howls. However, I am convinced that they do communicate, and it seems likely that this may have had some effect on the animal's ability to adapt to all sorts of conditions. I am personally convinced that coyotes often howl for the pure pleasure of it and that, at times, they howl because they are lonely.

30

Meet the Coyote

In areas where coyotes are numerous, loud and sudden noises will start them howling. Furthermore, certain sounds will stimulate them in much the same way as they would a dog. Some friends of mine who raised a coyote pup had a couple of youngsters seven or eight years old. Their high-pitched voices had just the right sound to stimulate howling. The children often imitated a coyote howl, to the best of their ability, and the pet would throw back his head and reply.

Coyotes also bark. To me it sounds very much like the bark of a dog. They also seem to use the bark for a different purpose than the howl. I once watched and listened to a coyote in Yellowstone Park that had apparently taken an aversion to some large and noisy road construction equipment. About two hundred yards from where the bulldozers and trucks were working, the coyote took up a stand on a large boulder and barked. How long it had been sounding off before I arrived I don't know, but when I tried to move in close for a picture, it trotted over a hill and out of sight. Its barks sounded as if it was registering a complaint.

Though it seems at times contradictory to this animal's grim will for survival, the coyote is extremely playful. Observers have watched pups outside the den playing in the same manner as young dogs. If the female stays around for a time, they play with her—romping, pulling at her fur, and tumbling about. Captive coyote pups I have watched act no differently than a dog of the same age and enjoy about the same things. Coyotes seem to retain much of this playful instinct even after they are grown.

On a winter trip to Yellowstone Park some years ago (a fine place to observe coyote behavior at almost any time of the year) I watched five coyotes playing in the snow. I guessed that they were litter mates nine or ten months old at the time. They chased each other, indulged in mock fights, and rolled and tumbled. It was difficult to visualize these playful animals as an organized hunting pack.

Ed Park, who is a keen and accurate observer of wildlife, hand-raised

31

The World of the Coyote

a female coyote pup, and the stories he tells of her playful ways and intelligent actions are at times unbelievable. One of the animal's favorite games was vying with Park when both would try to grab some object, usually a rolled-up newspaper. He describes how the fast reaction of the animal enabled her to beat him every time. In time, he began to win occasionally. At first he thought he was getting a lot faster until he became convinced that the coyote was *letting* him win.

Coyotes sometimes play by throwing objects into the air and catching them. I once watched one toss a field mouse into the air repeatedly. Finally, after about ten minutes, it tired of the game and ate the mouse.

Tame coyote playing with a springer spaniel.

Spring

IN THE NORTHERN parts of the United States, Coyotes begin to bear their young in early April; somewhat later in southern areas. Yet within each section considerable variation exists. Most pups are born in dens, though in some warm sections of the country a sheltered spot above ground may be selected by the female. When this occurs, the young are usually soon moved by the parent to an underground den.

Whelping is the only purpose for which the coyote uses a den. Most of the time adult coyotes sleep on the ground in a protected spot. Even after the pups are born, the adults sleep outside the den and only spend time inside to feed the young.

Dens are located at almost any place that affords protection. Occasionally, they are surprisingly close to ranch buildings and roads. They have been found on level ground, hillsides, washouts, canyons, in rock bluffs and rock rims, under deserted buildings, in drainage pipes and culverts, and even in hollow trees.

There seems to be no particular rationale for the selection of den sites, though coyotes will often return to the same locality and, if not disturbed, will use the same den year after year. Males that have lost their mates may bring new ones to dens; however, according to Ernest Thompson Seton: "It is the mother who selects the den."

Most dens are located within easy reach of water. A readily available food supply is vital because of the additional needs of the nursing female and the pups.

It has been said that coyotes do not always establish their dens near

33

This natural rock den filled with water during wet seasons.

water. Dens in the large deserts of eastern Oregon were as far as 6 miles from water, but I do not consider this typical. In this section of the country, denning time, April 1 to June 1, is also the time of the year when precipitation is heaviest and most frequent. Wet snows and spring rains and the thousands of natural small catch basins in the area's many lava outcroppings provide myriad natural drinking places. Spring rains replenish these often enough to provide all the water coyotes need.

35

Entrance to a coyote den under an old log.

A natural rock den which contained pups in 1963.

Coyote drinking from a lava rock catch basin in the desert country of eastern Oregon.

Although coyotes may dig their own dens, they are opportunists and, where possible, will enlarge or remodel abandoned rabbit, badger, or fox burrows. Like domestic dogs, they are good diggers with their front feet, especially if the dirt is loose. Though they often utilize natural rock caves that require no digging, a typical excavated den is from 1 to 2 feet in diameter and from 5 to 30 feet long. The chamber or den proper is at the end of the tunnel and is somewhat larger than the passageway. Though this main chamber may occasionally contain nesting material of grass or fur, it is usually bare. Sometimes there is

36

An average size litter of six coyote pups. These are probably about three weeks old, and their fur is a dark cinnamon-brown color.

more than one opening to the den. These are generally well concealed by brush, and dens often have a hole in the ceiling for ventilation.

Coyotes start digging and cleaning their dens several weeks prior to whelping. The female usually prepares additional dens, and by the time the young are born, she may have a dozen or more ready for occupancy. Barren females sometimes prepare dens even though they are not traveling with a mate. Females that have lost pups will clean out several dens before realizing the futility of their efforts.

In excavating, the coyote pushes dirt backward through the tunnels and out the entrance where it forms a low, fan-shaped mound. Adult coyotes usually detour around this mound when approaching the den entrance.

Coyotes are born during the early part of April in the North, though young females may give birth to their first pups later. According to Ralph S. Palmer, females begin breeding when two years old. Stanley P. Young says there is evidence that they breed when they are a year old.

In the spring of 1963, Federal predator hunters in Morrow County, Oregon, found coyote dens containing pups on the thirteenth, fourteenth, twenty-sixth and twenty-eighth of March. Carl McDaniel, predator control trapper at Heppner, Oregon, reported finding a den on March 22, 1944, containing eleven pups that he estimated to be one month old. On March 8, 1946, he states, he dug six pups out of a den that he estimated had been born around February 14. In 1958, McDaniel found eleven dens containing sixty-six pups, all of which, he stated, were born in March.

These reports show earlier pup births than any other records I have been able to find. They indicate a mating date in early January or December. These 1963 dens averaged eleven pups per litter, which is unusually high.

Darrell Gretz, of the predator and rodent control branch of the U. S. Fish and Wildlife Service, advised me that government hunters

Spring

have found many dens around April 1 with pups that appear to be at least two weeks old. Also, according to Gretz, in his district in central Oregon, whelping time will vary as much as two months. This might be due to variations in altitude and temperature.

The number of pups in a litter is usually five to seven, but litters of nine to twelve are not uncommon. The largest litter on record was in Utah and numbered nineteen. The largest litter I have seen had ten youngsters in it. Female coyotes carry the pups for a gestation period of sixty to sixty-three days.

The proportion of male to female coyotes is about one to one, which

Coyote pups three to four weeks old.

The World of the Coyote

is about the same ratio as that of other predators such as wolf, mountain lion, and bobcat. The sex ratio of 56,595 coyotes killed in Arizona over a period of twenty-seven years was 52.3 males to 47.7 females.

Some wildlife students hold that vitamins may possibly be controlling factors of size and sex ratio of litters. It is generally recognized that a food shortage or an unbalanced diet has some effect on reproduction: little available food means small litters. Yet Stanley P. Young notes that in Arizona, where food conditions are ideal all year round, the average litter is still only five in number. However, this would not seem to eliminate the possibility that the starvation diet faced by

Coyote pup about four or five weeks old.

This pup has plenty of spunk. Note the white marking on its chest.

northern coyotes in heavy snow country and under extreme winter conditions would have an adverse effect on the spring litters.

Victor H. Cahalane states: "In June, 1945, after an open winter with little loss of game, seven coyote dens in Yellowstone Park were dug open. The seven dens contained only a total of twenty-five pups. The mothers, who had been undernourished all winter, had produced scarcely more than three pups apiece. This was far below the normal average of five or six."

Coyote pups are born blind and helpless. Their fuzzy, woolly fur is a dark gray on the back and upper parts. The head is a shade or

41

two lighter, and the under parts are somewhat paler with a light colored spot on the throat and one on the chest. The tail is the same dark gray as the back, tapers slightly, and is thinly covered. This coloration changes rather quickly, and by the time the pups have their eyes open, they're usually a dark cinnamon-brown.

For two or three days after the pups are born, the female apparently stays close to them while the male brings food to her. Thereafter the two may hunt as a pair. The pups' eyes open when they are nine to fourteen days old, according to Stanley P. Young. The pupil is round, compared with the vertically elliptical pupil in both red and gray foxes.

The pups suckle for three to eight weeks but begin to eat meat after about five weeks. The first meat in their diet is usually predigested and regurgitated by the parents, and provides a supplement to the mother's milk. If the tunnel is not too steep, the pups will emerge from the den approximately three weeks after they are born. At that age they are still weak and wobbly. However, at six weeks of age, they have all the playfulness of domestic puppies. They spend a great deal of time outside the den wrestling with each other, worrying old bones, digging, and sleeping in the sun.

The parent coyotes do their hunting in early morning and late evening; during the day they usually station themselves a short distance away from the den and keep watch on the surroundings. Their eyes can see if there is anything dangerous approaching from one direction, while their acute senses of hearing and smell can detect danger signals from another. These lying-up places around the den will be changed as the wind direction changes. When the adult coyotes approach the den, they prefer to do so against the wind and usually circle it in order to test the wind all around. Similarly, females examine the ground around the mouth of the den each time they return.

As the pups get older and stronger, their sorties around the den entrance will take them farther and farther away. However, they re-

Spring

main very much alert and scramble back into the den at the first sign of danger. Like all pups, they seem to be hungry most of the time and will make little pathways to nearby vantage points, where they sit and watch for the return of their food-bearing parents. After the pups are weaned, they require a great amount of meat. The parent animals then eat all they can hold from their kill and carry large pieces back to the den in their mouths. They drop what they have carried and regurgitate food they have eaten.

Coyotes have keen, well-developed senses and are usually aware of a man approaching long before he sees them. At such times, the animals remain quiet and stay hidden until the potential danger is gone. Then they are likely to move the youngsters to another den.

A young coyote hunting. This picture was made on June 13 when the pup was eight to ten weeks old. It was dull fulvous in color but the black tip of its tail was evident.

The World of the Coyote

Consequently, it is a rare opportunity for a competent observer to have a chance to study den activity of a coyote family without their being aware of it. For this reason a report by Arthur L. Cooper of Klamath Falls, Oregon, a hunter for the predator control division of the U. S. Fish and Wildlife Service, is of considerable interest. Mr. Cooper was called by a rancher who had been losing lambs to a coyote. The animal's tracks were small, which made Mr. Cooper think it might be a female. Because it was also coyote denning time, he started looking for one. He reached a rocky rim overlooking a canyon and sat down to examine the opposite slope through a binocular.

"I looked for about twenty minutes," Cooper relates, "before I saw what looked like a ground hog in a hole looking out. Soon it looked like two were there. It was about 1,000 yards off so I wasn't sure what they were, so kept watching for awhile. Then I saw a coyote come limping up the draw towards the den about 250 yards from the bottom. When she got about 25 yards from the den, she must have whined or something because the pups just poured out of the den and ran down to her. She regurgitated some food for the pups which they ate immediately. Then she lay down and they nursed for about three minutes. She got up and walked up above the den and lay down. One of the pups went in the hole and two came up to her for more lunch and she knocked them away. They went scampering through the sage brush while three went playing up the hill."

Edson Fichter had a somewhat similar experience with Nebraska coyotes. "Two coyotes came out of the den at about 5:15; in a few minutes six pups were above ground and playing about the den entrance. At 6:15 the adult female was sighted three-fourths of a mile to the north; she was not traveling directly toward the den, but appeared to be foraging. She reached the den at 6:48. The pups had been out of sight in the den for some minutes, but now were immediately out and at their breakfast. She nursed them standing up, and their hunger was satisfied in three minutes. The bitch remained at the den site about one-half hour, lying down, wandering about, nosing and licking her pups. The young were full of play, two or three of them always tussling vigorously with the adult when she was lying down. She left to the northwest going down the ravine and out of sight at 7:15."

Dens will occasionally contain two litters of different ages; rarely will there be three litters in a single den. Where two litters are present, one will often be much older than the other. Many observers suggest that the smaller pups belong to a young female, because they ordinarily whelp some two weeks later than the older females. It has also been pointed out that the young female, unable to locate a den of her own, has moved in with her mother. Also, since only one male is usually found around a den containing two litters, it is probable that he is polygamous and has sired both litters.

Darrell Gretz told me of finding two litters in a den in central Oregon's Jefferson County only a few miles from my home. There were eleven pups in what appeared to be a three- or four-week-old litter, and eight pups, only minutes old, in the second litter. He located the den while the young were being born.

Weldon B. Robinson and Maynard W. Cummings report that occasionally several adult coyotes are found at dens. The theory that such groups are composed of parents and their previous year's young seems substantiated by the fact that two, and possibly three, tagged coyotes, recognized by their cropped right ears, were observed at a den together with a pair of mated coyotes. A litter of three pups had been tagged in that vicinity the year before, and the crop-eared coyotes obviously were the pups of the previous season, still with their parents.

Unless one of the parent animals has been killed, a pair will normally be found near each den. However, the male has little to do with the pups until they are big enough to leave the den. Male coyotes have been seen bringing rabbits and rodents to the den entrance but these were undoubtedly intended for the nursing female inside. If the

45

female should be killed at nursing time, the young would not survive. However, if the pups are old enough to eat meat, the male takes care of them.

Male coyotes have been observed coming out of dens which contained young. Just what the male does in a den is not known. We have seen that the male coyote's function in family life does not require his presence in the den. However, both male and female will move pups when danger threatens. This could require the male's presence inside the den when the pups are small.

Coyotes move their young to other dens quite readily. This may explain why the female cleans out several prior to whelping. Coyotes are clean about their dens and there is little refuse or odor. Occasionally they move the pups to another den to get away from an infestation of fleas.

I once inspected a natural den location in a rocky canyon in central Oregon's Grant County. A litter of pups had been taken from this den the previous spring. But at the time I saw it, during a fast thaw of a heavy winter snow, there was a pool of water standing in part of the rocky tunnel. It was an ideal location except for a leaky roof and poor drainage. In any event, if this occurs during the time the pups are small, the parents would undoubtedly move the young ones to a drier spot in a hurry.

Though most of the time pups are moved relatively short distances, a male coyote was once observed moving four pups, one at a time, to another location 5 miles away. He accomplished this in a single night, requiring 40 miles of travel.

A female coyote will take great risks to protect her young. For example, a single pup, estimated to be about eight weeks old, was captured by a rancher while it was playing outside a den. He took the animal home and fastened it out of doors with a chain snapped to the metal ring of a leather collar. The next morning the pup was gone, along with the collar. The chain with the snap was still intact. Adult

A rocky rim on this coyote's hunting route comes in for some close scrutiny.

coyote tracks were thick around where the pup had been. It was the rancher's guess that the female had come after the pup and, in trying to chew off the collar, had accidentally opened the snap.

As the pups grow and become stronger, they gradually widen their travels from the den. It is now that their training in hunting begins. I am inclined to think that their curiosity and natural hunting instincts are used by them on insects outside the den. It is through practice in stalking and leaping on these that they learn most of the techniques that stand them in good stead later.

47

The World of the Coyote

Both parents participate in their youngsters' education. They teach them by example to capture ground squirrels, mice, and other small prey. During this time the dark cinnamon color of the pelt of a young coyote fades as it grows older. At eight to twelve weeks it has become dull fulvous in color with just an indication of the rusty, black and white color accents found in the pelt of a mature animal. Stanley P. Young believes that this is about the age when the family abandons the den and the entire family moves about, remaining together until early fall.

At eight to twelve weeks, the black-tipped overhair has not yet developed and the underfur predominates. The over-all effect is pale and drab, blending well with the pup's surroundings, especially in desert areas.

Coyote pups, like domestic dog pups, are highly appealing, and a great many people have made, or attempted to make, pets out of them. There is evidence to indicate that Indian tribes domesticated the coyote several hundred years ago.

Pet coyotes are not uncommon. When captured young they are easy to tame and adapt readily to domestic surroundings. While still young they are like puppies, but as they grow older they show some of the wariness of their wild cousins. Usually they are somewhat shy around strangers and are, not infrequently, one-man pets.

I cannot recommend coyotes as pets. Most people do not have the understanding or patience that wild pets of their size and temperament demand. The life of a domesticated coyote almost always ends tragically for the animal.

I remember talking to some cowboys in eastern Oregon who were bothered by a coyote that stole their lunches while they worked in the hay fields. The culprit was an animal that had been captured as a small pup and raised to near maturity. Then, because it was too much trouble, it was turned loose to fend for itself. The animal's future was bleak. It had lost its fear of people. Not too long afterwards it

This tame coyote is taking it easy on the couch.

49

was shot by a rancher who was surprised that a coyote would sit looking at him, "rather friendly like," no more than 30 yards away.

My friend Ed Park has great affection and an affinity for all wild-life. He and his wife, Ruth, kept "Yip," their coyote, for a year. During that time they became quite fond of the animal, and she appeared to return their affection. However, with strangers about, the coyote was extremely cautious and wary. While at home, Yip was penned on an enclosed back porch separated from the rest of the house by a solid wooden door. If visitors came who were strangers to her, she would remain perfectly quiet. However, if the visitor happened to be someone with whom Yip had previously made friends, she would raise a racket on the porch to indicate she wanted to come in.

Park remarked upon what he thought was her surprising intelligence and said she seemed to have a strong "sixth sense." As an example he pointed out that when he returned home unexpectedly, the coyote seemed to know he was coming, minutes before he arrived. Mrs. Park, not knowing that Park was coming, could in no way communicate this to the animal. She said that Yip would suddenly start running about the house, jumping up excitedly to look out of the windows. In a few minutes, Park would arrive.

The Parks were never able to housebreak Yip. They thought this might have been due to the fact that they could not let her be outside as one could a dog. Park also said that Yip had no unpleasant natural odor, certainly not like that of a cocker spaniel he had once owned. The coyote was never given a bath, yet always seemed to be clean.

Yip wanted to play with all the neighborhood dogs, but they seemed to be frightened of her. However, she was not as friendly towards cats. When a kitten was brought to the house one day, it took some quick work to keep the coyote from killing it.

A dislike for cats is not true of all pet coyotes. I watched a four-month-old coyote play with a tiny kitten, and it seemed to have no desire to hurt its playmate. The two grew up together, and the last I heard, they were still fast friends.

50

Spring

Duke Warner of Bend, Oregon, told me of a litter of nine coyote pups that he and his brothers raised when they were youngsters on a farm in eastern Colorado. The pups were about two weeks old when found and just barely had their eyes open. At home, their small male fox terrier took over the job of raising them. The dog was extremely protective and would not let any of the other farm animals near the pups.

The coyotes were never confined and were allowed to run free on the ranch. They would come when whistled for, but as they grew older some became quite shy. Considerable variation in their individual acceptance and tolerance of people was noticed. Some could be petted anytime while others were skittish and would stand away. One male coyote would hardly allow itself to be touched.

The youngest of the nine Warner boys was only one-and-a-half or two years old at the time. Since the weather was warm and their farm was remote, it was not unusual to allow the baby to go about unclothed. Duke remarked that he was always a bit bothered to see the child running around naked and playing with a pack of nine coyotes. Oddly, the coyotes would tolerate the baby more readily than the others in the family. Even the male coyote that was so shy would permit the baby to pet it.

Three of the pups were eventually sent to zoos. Neighbors took three for pets, and the remaining three were all eventually killed by farmers in the area.

I became well acquainted with a single coyote that had been raised on a large cattle ranch on the high desert of central Oregon. It also had been allowed to grow up with complete freedom. There were several dogs on the ranch, including some Australian shepherd pups, which the young coyote played with. A favorite stunt of the shepherd pups was to grab the young coyote at the base of his tail. They had done this so much that the fur there was noticeably worn.

I first saw the coyote when it was a year old. It was a big handsome animal though its pelage was showing some spring fade. There were two youngsters in the family that raised the coyote, and they were his devoted pals. However, in their familiarity, the coyote had set limits beyond which the youngsters dared not go. He had never bitten them, nor anyone else, for that matter, but his threats were so convincing on being annoyed that no one cared to call his bluff.

The cowhands on the place told me that the coyote had turned out to be a better hand at rounding up cows than the shepherd dogs. However, it eventually got too enthusiastic about its cattle herding. One day I received a call for help from the coyote's owners. The animal was beginning to bother the cattle too much. They were afraid it would turn vicious, and they wanted to get rid of it.

At about that time I had been notified indirectly that a Hollywood producer needed a coyote. I recommended this one. The animal soon became a TV star and, according to a letter I received from the producer, did a fine job.

A number of states have imposed restrictions of one kind or another on owning coyotes. These usually prevent the importation of coyotes into a state, or require a permit to keep one in captivity. The coyote's well-deserved reputation for adaptability and for moving into new country has prompted some of these laws.

Nowhere are coyotes given any legal protection; everywhere there is open season on hunting or trapping them. In some states hunting licenses are required just to be in the field with a gun regardless of the quarry, and trapping licenses are required for trapping any fur-bearers. These laws, however, are not designed to protect the coyote.

Summer

By June, when summer officially arrives, many coyote pups will be from eight to ten weeks old, extremely active, and on a meat diet. During the warmer months to follow, if they have not left the den with the adults, they will spend more and more time outside the den playing and learning their lessons by chasing insects and hiding in response to real or imaginary danger signals.

Sometime before fall they leave the den permanently and will take up the serious business of individually earning a living.

A study was made in Yellowstone Park of a family of coyotes consisting of parents and their four- to five-month-old pups. They were feeding in a meadow and were found to be eating a great many grasshoppers. A study of their droppings, in which the insects occurred up to 100 per cent in over half their scats (dried feces), suggested that the pups ate many more insects than their parents. Unquestionably grasshoppers would make good training material for pups which later must outrun quick and elusive rodents.

I recall seeing my own dog as a pup test his reflexes on all sorts of insects. Orphaned coyotes which have learned the art of insect hunting can often survive on this diet if they can locate water and avoid enemies.

During the two- or three-month period after leaving their den, the education of the pups continues. They become good hunters, well able to provide for themselves. Undoubtedly, they also learn about enemies and how to avoid them. The family breaks up gradually. The

53

The World of the Coyote

young ones may travel about in twos and threes for a while, but eventually they scatter. Occasionally, they may even remain together as more or less a family unit through the first winter.

The coyote seems to spend most of its waking hours in search of food. Both its appetite and curiosity are insatiable. It hunts in the evening, at night, and in the early morning. Most of the daylight hours it spends resting in some secluded nook—generally a hidden one that provides it a view of the surrounding country.

Each coyote has its own special hunting route or runway. The larger wolves follow a runway that is much longer than that of the coyote,

A coyote knows his hunting runway intimately.

Summer

which may cover no more than 10 miles. Unless something happens to draw it away, the coyote's runway will usually be within a short distance of the spot where it was born.

The abundance of food, or the lack of it, is the principal factor that determines whether or not the coyote leaves the runway for more productive areas. Given sufficient food, a coyote may use the same runway throughout its life. The combination of game and livestock trails, old roads, and ditch banks that comprise the animal's hunting route will become as familiar to it as our own backyard to us. It knows all the nooks and crannies in its territory; the places to hunt and the

I watched this animal hunt a long stretch of rimrock without success.

The World of the Coyote

places to hide; where to drink water and where to wait. The coyote's progeny will be born and raised in the same area, and they will in turn learn the secrets of the country from their parents.

Several years ago in the Hampton Buttes section of the central Oregon desert country I watched a beautifully furred coyote making its daily rounds. It was diligently hunting the upper edge of a small canyon. Every likely spot where a prey animal might be received its attention. I could soon tell that it had been there many times before. I sat quietly 75 yards away on the opposite rim. The coyote never saw me while it hunted a full quarter of a mile of rim without success.

Persecution by man will drive a coyote away from its runway and into unfamiliar country. Severe winter weather may also force the coyote to abandon familiar country temporarily; but with the changing of seasons it will migrate back to its former hunting grounds.

The hunting ability of a coyote is legendary, and most observers feel that it is a firm believer in using brains rather than brawn. The coyote seems to approach each new potential food item with the theory

A young coyote hunting along the edge of a stream. It's probably looking for mice.

that it may be edible. Strange and indigestible things have been found in coyotes' stomachs. Its willingness to experiment has undoubtedly enabled it to add many new and nourishing foods to its diet.

Open meadows and mountain parks are favorite coyote hunting grounds. Here they spend many hours searching for mice and other small rodents. They move along slowly, and when they sight their quarry, they freeze for a moment before pouncing on it. Usually they are after a field mouse or a ground squirrel. Sometimes they miss with their first leap and must try again and again. If a coyote is successful, it holds its prey against the ground with its front paws until it is able to get the animal in its mouth. Sometimes this takes some doing, as the rodent is often under a heavy matting of grass.

I once watched a coyote hunt for ten minutes or so before it finally caught something. Although I could not see what it was, it must have been larger than a field mouse, more likely a ground squirrel. The coyote ate it in three gulps and then went back to hunting for more.

Coyotes are quick to see the possibilities in any situation that might

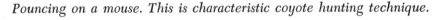

Pouncing on a mouse. This is characteristic coyote hunting technique.

The World of the Coyote

provide them with easy meals. In southern California a farmer became quite friendly with a coyote that followed the irrigation water on his farm and picked up pocket gophers that were flooded out of their holes.

Three biologists on a western range field trip came upon a small herd of cattle grazing in rather tall grass; they saw a large coyote walking calmly along with the cattle. The coyote was using the cattle as beaters to flush its game and was grabbing and eating the mice, rabbits, and other small creatures that moved from cover before the grazing herd.

In Yellowstone Park, coyotes have been seen following snowplows. As the plows cleared the roads of snow, the coyotes caught field mice that the plowing exposed.

Another observer watched for an hour while a coyote let a great bull elk act as his "game flusher." The elk was using his hooves to dig down through the snow to grass. This disturbed the mice, and as they ran off, the coyote grabbed them. Several times the anxious coyote dived under the old bull's belly to snatch up a speeding mouse.

Hunting rodents in heavy cover.

Summer

Grinnell, *et al.*, reported the hunting methods of a coyote on meadows in California's Yosemite National Park. They noted one stepping cautiously along the edge of a snow patch that covered a meadow. It would stop, then leap into the air and come down on the snow with all four feet bunched together. In so doing the coyote packed down the snow, thereby blocking the tunnels used by meadow mice. He was then able to dig them out before they could get away. Hunting was so good that the first coyote was joined by a second before the day was over.

A coyote once became the constant companion of a busy bulldozer. As the big piece of equipment worked at clearing a thicket of brush, the coyote stood by to catch the rodents flushed out of the heavy cover.

Lester Abbie is an employee of the National Park Service. He has been in Yellowstone Park for thirty years. His connection with the equipment maintenance department has kept him out on the roads of the park during all seasons of the year. This has given him an opportunity to observe a coyote's hunting techniques at first hand. Some of these are so unique that one must conclude that a coyote's greatest attri-

A successful hunter.

The World of the Coyote

bute as a hunter is its ability to solve new problems it meets each day.

One winter day, Abbie was running a snowplow into the "Old Faithful" section of the Park. He had stopped for lunch on a slight hill overlooking the Firehole River and was parked about 75 yards from the water. Wild mallards were swimming about on the river, which is open during the winter because it is fed by hot springs. The ducks were feeding on underwater vegetation. As they ducked their heads to feed, the current carried them downstream until eventually they were beyond the underwater weed bed. They would then fly

Snow with a crust strong enough to hold a coyote gives the animal a great advantage, especially when it is hunting weakened big-game mammals.

back upstream, alight in the water, and again float downstream over the underwater plants.

While Abbie leisurely ate his lunch, he noticed a coyote walking along the opposite side of the river. The coyote saw the mallards and immediately stopped in his tracks. He did not move so much as a hair until the ducks had floated past and were out of sight down the river. Then he trotted forward a few feet and stopped again as the birds left the water and flew back up the river to start their float downstream again. Once more the coyote remained absolutely still until the birds were out of sight. After three tries he reached the water's edge at the point where the ducks came by nearest to the shore.

From his vantage point on the bank, which was about a foot above the water, the coyote stretched out over the water and waited as the birds floated by. However, he was not in the right position and did not move as the feeding birds passed. After they were out of sight, he changed his position, but it still did not suit him. He was within a foot or so of the ducks each time they passed, but they paid no attention to the coyote.

Finally, after about six attempts, the coyote was perfectly located. As a big green-headed drake floated under the coyote, he opened his mouth and closed it on the mallard's head. With the duck dangling from his jaws, the successful hunter trotted away.

On another occasion, an observer watched while a coyote crawled up the edge of a creek where ducks were feeding. The coyote dove into the water. This frightened the ducks and they all dove under the surface. After a short time the ducks surfaced and flew away. The coyote then came up with a duck in its mouth.

Along with magpies, crows, ravens, buzzards, and eagles, the coyote has discovered that our modern highways are a source of food, providing great numbers of car-killed rabbits, birds, and other animals. In Oregon, hundreds of jack rabbits are killed each night on highways.

The World of the Coyote

In addition, many deer and some antelope are also killed each year by traffic.

Rabbits make up a substantial part of a coyote's menu, but in pursuing long-legged western jack rabbits, a single coyote has considerable trouble catching them. However, coyotes generally hunt jack rabbits in pairs with one coyote relieving the other from time to time during the chase. If the jack rabbits ran in a straight line, it is likely they could escape, but they tend to circle and this gives the coyote relay team a chance to catch them.

Duke Warner was fortunate to be on hand when his 3½-month-old pet coyotes demonstrated their abilities in team hunting for jack rabbits. Warner took the two coyotes with him one day when he went to bring back the cows to ranch headquarters. On the way, they flushed a jack rabbit that quickly bounded over a slight hill ahead of them.

The coyotes looked at each other for a moment, Warner said, then one ran after the rabbit while the other ran off to one side around the hill. Warner dashed to the top of the hill to see what happened, but by the time he got there the two young coyotes had the rabbit. He was unable to tell which one had actually made the catch.

Lester Abbie told me another story of coyote cooperation resulting in a rabbit dinner. Each winter Mr. Abbie feeds rabbits around his home at the Yellowstone Park headquarters. The snow is often deep, and food is scarce and hard to come by for all animals. One of the rabbits living from Abbie's handouts had a hideout under the house. Each day a coyote came by and made a half-hearted pass at the rabbit, which would immediately run to its haven.

One morning Abbie heard the rabbit squeal. He looked out the window and saw a coyote trotting off with the rabbit in its mouth. A different coyote had caught the rabbit, but the original one was also there. The strange coyote ate about half the rabbit, then left it for coyote number one to finish. From the tracks left by the animals, it is Mr. Abbie's belief that after getting the rabbit accustomed to his presence each morning, the first coyote brought another to the place and stationed him near the hole under the house. When the first coyote again chased the rabbit, it ran directly into the jaws of the coyote waiting by the house.

Vernon Maw, biologist for the Oregon State Game Commission, told me of an experience he had which involved a different method used by a coyote to get a jack rabbit. Mr. Maw was out one day in the open desert country of central Oregon when he saw a golden eagle dive at something on the ground. Through his binocular he saw that it was a coyote. The eagle dived again at the coyote, which dodged, then turned on its back, and presented its feet and snapping jaws to the diving bird. Maw said that the eagle must have dived at least thirty times at the coyote. Between dives the coyote would run a few feet, then turn to defend itself as the eagle struck at it again.

Finally, the coyote reached a shallow draw where the eagle could no longer get at him. Maw decided to find out what was going on. He walked to where he could see the coyote and shot him. Maw expected to find the coyote badly torn from the sharp talons of the eagle, but an examination revealed no wounds. He skinned the animal in order to make a more thorough examination and found no damage at all.

Near where the eagle had been making his attacks was a freshly killed jack rabbit. Maw examined it and found its only wounds were from the eagle's talons! Obviously, the eagle had killed the jack rabbit. It was either too large for the bird to make off with or else the coyote surprised the eagle before it had a chance to carry the rabbit away. In either case, it appeared certain that the coyote had stolen the jack rabbit from the eagle and that the eagle had been making an all-out effort to get it back.

There are many examples of coyotes hunting in pairs, especially when hunting larger animals. Sometimes one coyote of a hunting pair will try to attract the attention of a prey animal while the other coyote kills. In others, one chases while the other rests and then the positions

A coyote is at a great disadvantage in deep, soft snow like this. As can be seen from this animal's tracks, he can move only by leaping through the snow. This is much too slow to catch any game and is extremely tiring to the coyote.

will be reversed. Coyotes will occasionally attack deer, antelopes, and elk with young. One coyote will attract the attention of the mother animal and draw it far enough away from the young for the other coyote to make a quick attack and kill it.

Adult antelopes are hunted by two or more coyotes in much the same way coyotes hunt rabbits. Since the antelope usually circles when being chased, the coyotes cut across the circle and may eventually strike down the tired antelope.

Coyotes are not always successful when hunting antelopes. Two witnesses in an airplane in South Dakota saw a doe antelope with a kid being chased by a coyote. When the coyote got close to the kid, the doe dropped back and collided with the coyote, knocking it off its feet and rolling it on the prairie. The doe did this several times, thus enabling her youngster to get well ahead of the coyote.

The kid was soon joined by another doe which apparently had a fawn hidden nearby. The second doe led the kid over a hill and turned off with it in full view of the coyote. After doing this several times, the doe and kid went over the hill, then ran off in opposite directions. The coyote, some distance behind, was confused. He ran after the second doe, which thus enabled the kid to escape.

Sometimes the hunter may become the hunted. In another reported observation, eight mature Texas antelopes chased a coyote for 12 miles. Finally the coyote took refuge in a bush, but the antelopes pounded it with their sharp hooves until the coyote was dead.

Young deer, antelopes, elk, and the young of most domestic animals are easy prey for a mature coyote if he comes upon them away from their adults. However, attacking the adults is much more difficult. Unless the antelope is ill or injured, the coyote needs an advantage.

During periods of deep crusted-over snow, deer are much more vulnerable. They break through the crust and flounder about helplessly. The coyote, able to walk on top of the crust, is unhampered. Under such circumstances, a coyote can kill a large deer.

A mule deer buck in belly-deep snow can be killed by a coyote if the snow is crusty enough to hold him.

A doe and two fawns resting in the snow. Winter-weakened deer provide food for coyotes.

Summer

I have seen coyotes in Yellowstone Park close to both deer and antelopes, yet neither the antelopes, deer, nor coyotes seemed disturbed. I mentioned this to Lester Abbie. He believes that the coyote is always alert to the possibilities of killing nearby deer and antelopes and that when it strolls by it is checking to see if the animals are alert. Likewise, the deer and antelopes show no fear unless they feel there is a danger.

Mr. Abbie described the following incident that seems to support his theory. He was watching a small herd of deer feeding around the houses in Mammoth within Yellowstone Park. The snow was fairly deep but not so deep as to put the deer at a disadvantage. Two coyotes trotted by not too far from the feeding deer. Most of the deer looked at them without showing fear, though they may have been weighing the danger and were fully alerted.

An eight-month-old buck suddenly decided to show off, or so it seemed. He started prancing, got into a deep drift, and floundered about. The coyotes, seeing the young buck at a disadvantage, quickly attacked. Before Abbie could get out of the house to drive them away, the deer was too badly injured to be saved.

It is 5 miles from Mammoth Hot Springs to Gardiner, Montana, the north entrance to Yellowstone Park. All the way the road is steep and curving and in winter is often slick with packed snow. The road winds around the base of Mt. Everts, winter range of part of the Park's bighorn sheep herd. It was along this stretch one winter that Lester Abbie saw an example of pack-hunting by coyotes, if you consider a female and her five almost full-grown pups a pack. It also looked like a lesson in hunting.

While driving toward Gardiner one morning, Abbie saw several bighorn ewes and lambs a short way up the slope of the mountain. Nearby he saw a female coyote with what he decided were her five big pups. They would have been about ten months old at the time. The female coyote suddenly charged the band of bighorns and started them running. She then chased a young ram out of the flock and pursued it in circles. Then the young coyotes took up the chase while the female stood aside and watched. After the young ones had chased the lamb for a while, the female ran in and disabled it, at which the pups ran in to feed.

There have been many fanciful tales told about coyotes and badgers cooperating in the gathering of food. In most of the ones I have heard or read about, the badger seems to do all the work and the coyote contributes little but a big appetite. However, there is more than a modicum of truth to these stories. There seems to be some question as to just how much cooperation is involved in these mutual ventures, but there seems to be little doubt that coyotes and badgers have been seen together.

Few coyotes will attack a full-grown healthy badger. A badger is a

Fifty yards from these nine deer a pack of coyotes were playing, but it didn't seem to disturb these animals.

fine fighting machine and a good hunter. He is also as capable at digging as any animal you can find in the wild. This ability is, I think, the chief reason why coyotes and badgers are occasionally seen together. Coyotes can easily keep out of the short-legged badger's way. A badger probably learns this fairly early in life. When a coyote starts traveling with him, the badger probably accepts it. When he starts digging for ground squirrels or prairie dogs, the ones that escape his long claws and sharp teeth will likely be caught by the waiting coyotes.

A good example of coyotes' teamwork is the way they kill porcupines. A porcupine defends itself by turning its back toward the attacker and spreading the quills on its rear. While doing so it also swishes its heavily armed tail about.

Working as a team, a pair of coyotes will alternately make false charges at the porcupine. Each time it turns to present its armed rear

A coyote waits on the hillside for something to eat while two ravens fly by; behind him an antelope grazes unconcerned about it.

The World of the Coyote

to the danger. The coyotes, working from two sides, keep it shifting its rear about until finally it refuses to fall for the bluffed charges. Then one of the coyotes makes a real charge. He deftly and quickly slips a paw under the porcupine's chin and flips it over on its back, which exposes its soft, unprotected belly to attack.

Lester Abbie once watched a male and female coyote in one of Yellowstone Park's large meadows demonstrate another type of co-operation. The female was hunting mice, but the male merely stood and watched. Abbie then noticed that the male had a badly injured

This is a badger, which sometimes helps a coyote get an easy meal.

Coyotes hunting in pairs occasionally outsmart a porcupine and make a meal of one.

left shoulder and seemed unable to use its front left leg. Abbie guessed that the animal had been struck by a car.

The female was now catching mice with some regularity. Frequently the crippled male would hobble over to her on three legs and take a

The World of the Coyote

mouse she had just caught. Each time she gave up the mouse without protest. Abbie concluded that they were mates and that the female was taking care of her injured spouse.

When going after larger prey, the coyote usually rushes and attacks from the front and kills with a quick jab of its canines to the neck and throat of the animal, cutting the jugular vein. However, it will usually kill lambs by biting them through the head. Young inexperienced coyotes, like dogs, will attack their prey at any part of their body.

The bite of the coyote, which is much the same as that of the wolf and dog, derives its effectiveness from the relatively long, recurved, sharp-pointed canine teeth. The wounds inflicted by a coyote's bite can sometimes seem more severe than a mere "bite" would warrant. It appears that any tearing effect of the animal's sharp teeth and strong jaws is assisted by the weight and direction of movement of the animal involved.

When a coyote makes a leap at the throat of, say, a fleeting antelope, it will usually be going in the same direction as the antelope. After it sinks its teeth in the antelope's throat and falls towards the ground, the dead weight of the coyote pulls against the running antelope, producing a downward tearing action.

Darrell Gretz has examined many animals killed by coyotes; he told me that never has he seen anything but puncture wounds inflicted by a coyote's teeth. This is substantiated by my friend, Jim Ricci, who has had many years of experience taking care of zoo and other captive animals. Ricci states that a coyote's bite is a rapid series of bites resulting in multiple puncture wounds from the canine teeth.

The coyote is a ravenous eater and tears apart its prey, swallowing it in great chunks. The animal's carnassial teeth act like shears and enable it to cut away chunks of flesh. Anyone who has ever watched a dog biting on something with the side of its mouth will have seen the carnassials in action.

It has been said that a coyote will eat anything that doesn't eat him

72

The fighting equipment of a coyote.

first. That the food be digestible doesn't even seem to be a requirement. The coyote is, as we have seen, basically carnivorous, though at times it also eats large amounts of vegetable matter. In all its range the feeding habits of the coyote are much the same and its preference is usually for food that is easiest to get.

A most complete study of the food habits of coyotes was reported by Charles C. Sperry, U. S. Fish and Wildlife Service, in 1941. This study involved, primarily, the laboratory analysis of 8,339 coyote stomachs from seventeen western states taken at all seasons of the year during the five-year period 1931–1935. Actually, 14,829 stomachs were examined, but 2,025 were empty, 4,368 contained debris only, and 97 were from pups still feeding on milk alone. The remaining 8,339 contained food items and were used as a basis for the study.

As was expected, rabbits were the number one item in the diet, except during the winter when carrion took over the top spot. Rabbit was the principal coyote food in all seventeen states, and young rabbit was prominent in the diet of the young coyotes still being fed by adults.

Next to rabbits, carrion was the largest food item. For the most part this came from the remains of horses, cows, coyotes, and sheep. Coyotes ate more than twice as much carrion during the winter as during the summer.

The following taken from Sperry's report shows the relative volume of various foods found in the examined coyote stomachs.

	SUMMER	FALL	WINTER	SPRING	ANNUAL
Rabbits	29%	29%	33%	42%	33%
Carrion	17%	28%	36%	20%	25%
Rodents	22%	17%	13%	18%	18%
Sheep and goats	18%	14%	10%	13%	13.5%
Miscellaneous	14%	12%	8%	7%	10.5%
	100%	100%	100%	100%	100.0%

Jack rabbit, coyote prey, provides most of its food.

Young mule deer, occasional coyote prey.

Mallard duck, occasional coyote prey.

Ground squirrel, coyote prey.

Summer

Rodents, which were an important item, especially in summer, included meadow mice, wood rats, cotton rats, ground squirrels, marmots, pocket mice, kangaroo rats, pocket gophers, and porcupines.

Sheep and goats comprised the bulk of domestic livestock remains found in the stomach contents. Calf, colt, and pig (adults of larger domestic animals are so infrequently killed by coyotes that they were not considered) contributed less than 1 per cent. Undoubtedly, this percentage of sheep and goats consumed by coyotes gives an untrue picture when applied to the coyote population as a whole, for the stomachs examined came from control operations. This means that the trapped or killed coyotes were animals thought to be preying on domestic livestock.

Coyotes from areas where there were no sheep or goats and no control operations would not, of course, have any domestic livestock in their stomachs. By the same reasoning, the other percentages would

Antelope kid and its mother.

The World of the Coyote

also be somewhat distorted. This is of little concern except with big-game mammals or game birds. However, the percentages here were not large, and it is likely that elimination of the sheep and goat percentage for those coyotes away from livestock would not result in much of an increase in the percentage of big-game mammals and game birds present.

Big-game mammals comprised 3.63 per cent of the total, and this was mostly deer (3.58 per cent), a small amount of antelope (0.05 per cent), and just a trace of bear, bison, elk, and bighorn sheep. Consumption of deer reaches three distinct peaks each year: late in the winter, during the fawning period, and in the hunting season. There is considerable difference of opinion with respect to the deer-coyote relationship, which will be discussed at length a bit later. However, the peak period of deer meat consumption mentioned in Sperry's report would indicate that the coyote feeds more on deer in late winter because other foods are scarce, or because deer weakened by winter are easier prey, or because winter-killed deer are available as carrion; that during fawning season the young deer make easy prey; and that

A mature buck antelope like this one can outrun a coyote as well as give it rough treatment with his sharp hooves.

Mule deer fawns are favorite targets of the coyote.

Young coyote with a jack rabbit it has just caught.

during the hunting season remains from hunter kills, or cripples that get away, provide an easy addition to its diet.

The final list of small mammals revealed by stomach analysis shows such a variety that it would appear that almost anything is acceptable as food, and the only reason some of the items occur so infrequently is that individuals of these species are not available in large numbers. For example, the frequency of skunk remains in stomachs examined during the summer and fall indicates that the coyotes were probably not starving, and that they had been eating skunk by choice rather than necessity.

Birds, including poultry, occurred frequently but represent only a small percentage of the total volume of food. Chickens constitute most of the poultry, with other domestic fowl present in only token amounts. Game birds, both upland and waterfowl, contribute their share to a coyote's diet as do nongame birds. However, they represent a minor addition to the coyote's larder. Occasionally coyotes find a bonanza of birds, however, and then for a short time birds may well constitute all the food consumed by a small number of coyotes.

Such a situation came to my attention several years ago. I had spent some time photographing birds on a small island in Crump Lake in south-central Oregon. There were several hundred nesting white pelicans and a great band of raucous sea gulls along the beach area. The low, thorny, "greasewood" bushes that covered the higher center of the island held egret, heron, and cormorant nests. I let the birds rest for a couple of weeks and then returned for another photographic session and found the island barren of birds. During my absence, the water receded in the lake and made a peninsula out of what had previously been an island. Coyotes quickly found out about it and in just a few days had consumed all the young birds.

Reptilian remains were frequently found in coyote stomachs. These included several different kinds of snakes, including rattlesnakes, various lizards, and a few turtles. An occasional fish was present, but in

Cottontail rabbits furnish many a meal for the coyote.

Part of the pelican, egret, etc., rookery that the coyotes cleaned of nests after low water permitted them to get to the island.

all 8,339 stomachs examined, not a single frog was found. Insects were found often enough and of a kind to indicate that they were consumed in the serious business of eating and not just to satisfy the animal's curiosity. Grasshoppers were most common and in some instances formed a substantial part of the stomach's content. Seventy-one per cent of the last meal of a young coyote taken in southern New Mexico was grasshopper, and in an Arizona specimen there were 500 grass-hoppers.

Although some 98 per cent of all the food examined was animal matter, coyotes do eat some plant foods. This is deliberate and not because of a shortage of other foods. Some cultivated small fruit showed up in every month of the year, but in those months when wild fruit was available (July-October) it was four times as prominent. Also, during this same period fruits averaged twice the annual amount.

Domestic fruit for which coyotes have shown a liking include grapes, figs, prunes, pears, peaches, apricots, apples, and cherries. Outstanding items among the wild fruits are prickly pears, mesquite beans and pods, apples of hawthorn, juniper berries, persimmons, chokecherries, and others.

Coyotes display a fondness for watermelons and, according to some reports, have an uncanny ability to pick ripe ones.

The amounts of food sometimes eaten by coyotes are astounding. Four coyotes in Yosemite National Park, California, took approximately 75 pounds of meat from a doe deer weighing around 100 pounds at a single meal, and within thirty minutes. A 36-pound male coyote killed in New Mexico contained just under 12 pounds of sheep fat.

Sperry's study on coyote food habits revealed those things that a coyote ate, along with some indication of the variations between seasons and localities. However, in all cases it seemed quite obvious that the coyote was eating that food which was available and most easily obtained, not necessarily what it liked best.

Sage grouse suffer more from coyote predation than any other birds.

Coyote hunting along water.

The World of the Coyote

Eldon E. Whiteman conducted a study with captive coyotes to determine their actual food preferences:

"The coyotes showed a definite preference to mutton over rabbit. Both mutton and rabbit were eaten on all trials except one, when one individual buried the rabbit after eating the mutton. Preference was also shown for mutton over muskrat and for rabbit over venison. Mutton carrion was preferred just a little oftener than fresh meat."

A coyote is not at all squeamish about feeding on coyote carcasses. Western trappers have long known that a coyote carcass makes a fine lure to decoy living animals into a trap or to a poison station. However, there is no evidence to indicate that a pack will turn on some weak members. But if hungry enough, coyotes finding a weakened member of the clan in a trap are quite apt to dine well that day.

In much the same manner as dogs, coyotes will often bury food when they have more than they can eat at a single meal. Later they return to the spot, dig it up, and eat it. The coyote's need of water is undoubtedly affected to some extent by the kind of food it has been eating. From a fresh kill with moist flesh and blood, it would receive a lot of its needed moisture. On the other hand, old dried-out meat would furnish little moisture. Denning coyotes usually go to water once in twenty-four hours, but it is likely that during the warmer months, or after excessive exertion, a coyote will seek water more often.

In the dry country of the Southwest, coyotes will dig down 2 or 3 feet in the bottom of a dry wash in search of water and frequently find it. Travelers through dry sections are refreshed from wells discovered by coyotes. Darrell Gretz has told me that evidences of similar digging by coyotes and the discovery of water as a result has been seen in desert country of eastern Oregon.

The coyote is not at all afraid to enter water when necessary. It is recorded that coyotes swam the Columbia River at a spot where it is a half-mile wide for a chicken dinner, and that a Wyoming female coyote raided lambing sheep herds by swimming the Green River both ways—sometimes with a lamb clutched in her mouth.

Harold C. Bryant followed the tracks of a coyote that voluntarily swam a 30-foot channel, 8 feet deep, to reach nesting birds in the Salton Sea. The coyote ate parts of two mudhens and buried the remainder before returning to the mainland.

In the coyote all three senses—sight, hearing, and smell—are exceptionally keen; more so, it seems, than in many other animals. Joseph Grinnell and his co-authors in California state: "We do not believe that the coyote's sense of smell is notably keener than its sense of sight.

With extremely acute eyesight, hearing, and smell, a coyote is always alert to what is going on around it.

The World of the Coyote

Observations made with binoculars have shown that a coyote stalking meadow mice in an open meadow depends most on its sense of hearing to guide it to its prey."

A coyote is just as good at seeing as it is at hearing but often will not fear a nearby object if that object is absolutely stationary. There was an occasion when trapper Sam Shaver and I were searching for coyote dens on a large butte in eastern Oregon. We had separated and I was moving down off the butte looking for tracks. I stopped for a moment to study some fresh coyote tracks. Out of the corners of my eyes I saw a coyote moving across in front of me about 40 yards away. The animal trotted along obviously unaware of my presence. As it got directly below me on the slope, it stopped and looked uphill. Either the light breeze had warned it of my presence or it had distinguished me from the scenery. For several seconds the animal studied me while neither of us moved. Then it turned and galloped away. I suspect that

A coyote rolling on a long-dead and very smelly fish.

Summer

I made a slight movement of which I was unaware, but, regardless of what it was, it decided I was dangerous and made a quick exit.

A coyote has a great appreciation for smells and, like other members of its clan—dogs and wolves—loves to roll in material of strong odors. Most of these odors are offensive to man and come from such things as long-dead mammals, birds, and dead fish. My old beagle hound does the same; he has come home smelling so high that even a bath in heavy suds and liberal doses of the best deodorizers could barely make him acceptable. At other times I have watched him go over the lawn with his nose working like a vacuum cleaner until he located some vague odor that escaped me, then thoroughly roll in the place. Coyotes do the same. Often the delicate scent that lures them to a particular spot is far too elusive to be detected by man's relatively insensitive nose.

Indians also appreciated the coyote's sense of smell, and, according to one story, "When the legendary hero of the Yosemite Indians sought to give his son all of nature's virtues, he dressed him in a robe of coyote skins to make him keen-scented."

The coyote seems to have more than its share of diseases and parasites, almost all of which a domestic dog is equally susceptible to. Its curiosity, its omnivorous taste in food, and its uncanny ability as a

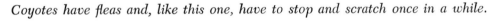

Coyotes have fleas and, like this one, have to stop and scratch once in a while.

scavenger expose the coyote to all sorts of things, and also make it possible for it to spread diseases and parasites.

Fleas, ticks, tapeworms, roundworms, lice, flukes, and mites—all take up residence in or on coyotes with varying degrees of harmfulness. Mange among young pups can be especially deadly. Sometimes the infection is so severe that adults lose almost all of their hair. This can be fatal on the coyote's cold, northern ranges.

Coyotes are also susceptible to distemper, tularemia, and salmon poisoning, which is caused by the salmon fluke. Coyotes get the fluke from feasting on dead and dying salmon during the salmon spawning runs up the rivers of the Pacific Northwest.

By far the most dreaded disease that can be contracted and spread by coyotes is rabies. It is an infectious disease spread from animal to animal and terminates fatally. It has been known among members of the dog family since earliest times. Indians of the Great Plains feared it. It is quite likely that recurring rabies epidemics were principal factors in controlling wolf and coyote populations back in the days before the white man came west. Certainly this disease, which could spread rapidly through a dense population of coyotes, would deplete their numbers quickly.

An epidemic of rabies among coyotes began in central California in 1909. During the next five years it spread into an area covering all of Oregon east of the Cascade Mountains, the open country of southern Idaho known as the Snake River plains, and all of northern Nevada. By the end of 1923, over 2,000 people in the infected area had been bitten and fifty-six of these bites resulted in death. Nevada was hardest hit, and in the years 1915 and 1916 livestock losses to rabid coyotes in that state were estimated at $500,000.

Trained hunters were sent into the infected areas. By 1919, coyotes had been killed off to such an extent that the epidemic was finally brought under control. Since then there have been occasional rabies scares, but these have been local and quickly controlled. It is doubtful that we will ever again have such a sufficiently dense coyote population to create a similar rabies epidemic, because of the constant predator control measures now being practiced by state and federal agencies.

Melanistic (blackish) and albinistic (white) coyotes are extremely rare. Among 1,672,604 coyotes taken by Fish and Wildlife Service hunters in the thirty-year period between July 1, 1915, and June 30, 1945, only 6 were albinos. This averages out to 1 albino for every 278,767 coyotes captured. The late William L. Finley, noted Oregon naturalist and wildlife photographer, raised a white coyote pup taken from a four-pup den in Oregon. It was his estimate that this coloring would occur once in 200,000 coyotes.

The white coyote raised by Mr. Finley was not a full albino, as its eyes were gray, not pink. Usually, when albinism occurs it affects only one pup in a litter, but in a litter taken in western Nebraska, four were albinos. The eyes were a milky blue rather than pink.

Dr. W. G. Manning and Jerry McCann, both of Bend, Oregon, were deer hunting high up on the eastern slope of the Cascades a few miles west of town. They found a white coyote that had been killed the day before. Dr. Manning described the animal to me as being pure white— that is, as pure as you generally find in the wild, with eyes a washed-out blue-gray. He estimated it to be about two-thirds grown, which would have made it around six months old.

The only record I have found of a black or melanistic coyote was one reported by Stanley P. Young. It was trapped in Colorado in the early 1920's. Its eyes were a milky blue color like those reported in some albinos.

Autumn

FALL IS A TIME of change for young coyotes. It is then that they become adults in size and appearance. They are almost as large as their parents and in their first, richly colored winter coats may even look like them. Although the family may stay together rather loosely, the young are mostly on their own. They must now face all the man-made and natural hazards without the experience of the parent animals to protect them. Their first fall and winter will be a time of testing.

We have no records of what the full potential life span of a coyote in the wild might be. Captive coyotes, protected from the hazards of living in the wild, appear to have about the same life span as both wild and captive wolves—about ten to eighteen years. Two coyotes in the National Zoological Park, Washington, D.C., lived to be fourteen years and several months old; another, fifteen years ten months; a third, eighteen years six months.

In New Mexico, of nine male coyotes captured and tagged on the Jornada Range Reserve, six were recovered after an average lapsed time of two years and five months for each. One of these, a pup when released, was recovered nine years and three days later. This suggests that in the wild a coyote may live for a year or two, or possibly up to ten years, but the hazards to their lives from men who war on them are very great. In all wild things, it is the virtually defenseless and in-experienced young that suffer the highest casualties. Intensive den hunting each spring by predatory control hunters takes a considerable toll of coyote pups.

Autumn

In the fall, the young coyote's coat begins to thicken and picks up the color accents of the adult; by the last of November the coyote has the full winter pelage of a mature animal. At this time of the year the fur is at its brightest.

As in many mammals, the coyote's pelage consists of soft, relatively short underfur, light tan or fulvous in color, and much longer and coarser guard hairs. These are tipped with black or dark brown. As might be expected, the northern subspecies have a much longer and denser fur than those from warm sections. I have observed coyotes during the winter, where temperatures drop to 20 or 30 degrees below zero; their coats were so heavy that the animals looked barrel-bodied and their legs seemed abnormally short. In Mexican and Central American species the pelage is so coarse as to be bristlelike.

The coyote carries its prime coat until late in February when the annual molt commences. By this time the bright colors of the previous fall have faded. The timing of the molt will vary somewhat, depending upon locality. The overhair goes first, beginning with the tail and

Young coyote in the fall (October 1). It looks and acts like an adult now.

When the young coyote is about sixteen weeks old, it is old enough to take care of itself. It is beginning to look like an adult, with its coat picking up rust and black color accents.

the base of the tail; next comes the lower portions of legs; then up the legs to the sides and then the back. Back and belly regions are last. New pelage consists of short harsh overhair and a short scanty coat of underfur. During August and September this lengthens and grows thicker.

The feet of a coyote are quite similar to those of a dog, but it makes a track that is more elongated and not so rounded as a dog track. There are four toes on each hind foot and five on each front foot. The first toe is rudimentary but bears a well-developed claw. The claws are nonretractable and rather blunt. They are good digging tools, especially in ground which is not too hard.

Dimensions of tracks will naturally vary with the size of an animal, but these reported measurements will indicate proportions. The hind-foot of one coyote was 1¾ inches wide and 2¼ inches long. Another had tracks that measured 2 inches wide and 2½ inches long. The stride of the first coyote was 13, 13, 12, and 13 inches, consecutively. ("Stride" means length of step and would be measured from the same spot on consecutive tracks of the same foot.) The stride of the second coyote, in soft snow along a hillside, was 18, 20, 21, and 22 inches consecutively.

Tracks made by walking or trotting coyotes will be in almost a straight line. However, the stride will be from 22 to 24 inches when trotting as compared with about 13 inches when walking. A coyote will clear from 30 to 40 inches at a lope and when running at top speed will cover from 6 to 10 feet at each leap. Coyotes usually travel at a trot but will break into a hard run when pressed. They seem to go like a streak when they really put their minds to it. With ears laid back and tail streaming behind, the coyote's body skims the ground with no lost bounding motion.

Hartley H. T. Jackson states that the coyote's speed while trotting normally is less than 20 miles an hour and that its fastest speed seldom exceeds 30 miles per hour. Coyote speeds have been mostly determined

94

The fur of a coyote. The long, black-tipped guard hair is almost 3½ inches long. The black tip is about ½ inch long; then there is a band of white, about ½ inch long. The guard hair has the same fulvous color as the fine-textured underfur which is almost 2 inches long. This sample was taken from the back of a coyote. From other areas the measurements and colors would possibly be different.

Front foot of a coyote, right, as compared with the front foot of an Australian shepherd dog of about the same size.

Hind foot of a coyote, right, as compared with the hind foot of an Australian shepherd dog of about the same size.

Coyote digging.

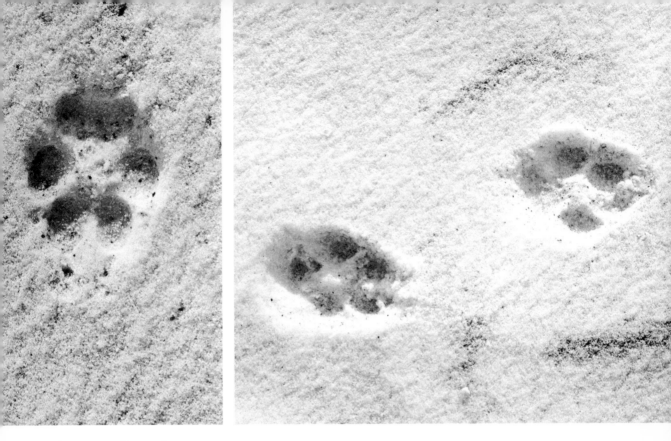

Coyote tracks, in the snow.

Coyote running at top speed.

by chasing them with automobiles, which generally produces a top speed maintainable only for short distances. These measured speeds are only as accurate as the vehicle's speedometer which usually shows a somewhat higher speed than is actually obtained. The fastest recorded speed determined by pacing with an automobile was 43 miles per hour. Others were 29 to 35 miles per hour.

An indication of the speed of a coyote compared with other mammals in their own habitats was obtained by Clarence A. Sooter by using automobiles in Malheur National Wildlife Refuge in Oregon. A two-point buck mule deer ran 35 miles per hour; a doe and two fawns, 28 miles per hour; and a coyote 29 miles per hour.

Several reports of the manner in which a coyote carries its tail under different circumstances seem to be in conflict. My own observations, supported by photographs, show that when the animal is standing and not disturbed, its tail hangs almost straight down and when moving about normally, or hunting at a trot, the tail is lifted at an angle of about 25 degrees above the perpendicular.

I have a series of pictures I took of a coyote running down the road ahead of my car in Yellowstone Park where high snowbanks on both sides prevented the animal from making his escape. He was pushed hard for at least a quarter of a mile before a break in the snowbank enabled him to get off the road.

While my companion steered the car, I made a series of pictures with a motor-driven sequence camera equipped with a 300-mm. telephoto lens. The resulting pictures, somewhat blurred because of the speed of the car and the dirty windshield, show that his tail was carried just a little lower than straight out behind him. Another series of pictures made of a pet coyote playing, but nevertheless running full tilt, showed the tail being carried in an almost identical manner.

I would conclude from these observations that a coyote carries his tail in whatever manner is natural or necessary to help do what he wants to do at the moment. When he runs at maximum speed, either

When the coyote stands, its tail hangs straight down.

A trotting coyote carries its tail just a bit below horizontal.

to capture a meal or escape danger, the tail flowing out behind probably provides less hindrance to speed than in any other position. Likewise, for trotting, the tail need not be lifted far back to be out of the way.

Although the coyote's greatest enemy is man, it has many others. While it is still a pup the weather, the great horned owl, the eagle, the timber wolf, possibly the badger, and others, may keep its career from ever getting started. The adult's enemies are the golden eagle, wolf, cougar, and bear. Adult coyotes have been killed by deer, antelope, and elk. Starvation takes a substantial number in areas where winters are severe.

Adolph Murie states: "Coyotes as a rule are too quick to be caught under the stabbing hooves of an elk or a deer, but fatalities of this kind have occurred." As an illustration he cites the report of a Yellowstone Park ranger who discovered a badly mutilated dead coyote with a broken back. Snow around the dead animal was extensively trampled, and the tracks showed that it was an elk that had killed the coyote.

George B. Grinnell reported the observation of an attack by a golden eagle on a full-grown coyote. The eagle dove on the coyote and apparently killed it quickly. However, the animal was much too large for the bird to fly off with. The observer drove the bird away and examined the coyote. Its throat was torn.

Charles C. Sperry tells of government predator trapper Charles S. Blanchard's discovery that a coyote in one of his traps had been attacked and killed by a group of javelinas which also tore up the carcass. This happened at a time when natural javelina foods were available.

Previously I mentioned that rattlesnake has been found in coyote stomachs to such an extent that one can conclude that they are a fairly frequent item of food, especially in the arid Southwest. Undoubtedly, some coyotes are bitten while trying to eat rattlesnakes, and we would assume that some of the animals succumb to the poison. However, it

100

Bobcats and coyotes share much of their United States range with little conflict.

Though black bears are found in some coyote habitats, they don't appear to constitute a threat.

The World of the Coyote

must be that many recover. It has been reported that a noticeable number of the coyotes trapped in Texas show the scars of healed rattlesnake bites. The scars are mostly on the front quarters, but some are on the hind legs and sometimes on the head.

In the North, where snows are a problem, starvation may take considerable toll of coyotes under certain conditions. During winters when the snow is soft and deep, deer with their long legs get around in good shape and are able to paw their way through the snow to forage beneath. However, coyotes, short-legged by comparison, are unable to move about well enough to catch anything. Since it might be a winter of little starvation for deer and other big game, there is little carrion available for coyotes. Eventually they become so weak from lack of food that they cannot even catch and kill a sick deer.

A coyote's best defense against his enemies is his wariness. It might also be said that his curiosity is his biggest weakness, as it may lead the animal into becoming trapped or poisoned. When cornered, a coyote can fight savagely and his teeth are formidable weapons. However, he would much rather avoid trouble than fight his way out of it. Characteristically the coyote is an extremely practical animal. He sees little

Only in very limited areas do the ranges of the grizzly bear and the coyote overlap. The bear might be a threat to the young while they are still in their den.

gain in taking chances for prey of dubious value. When possible he avoids trouble. If he can't avoid it, he will try to run away from it. If he cannot run away, he will fight.

The coyote's relationship with small predators is much the same as his relationship with large predators, except that the roles are reversed. As the coyote finds the large wolf or bear his enemy, so the smaller predators find the coyote their enemy. The fact that the smaller predators seldom fall prey to the larger ones is due to the fact that these animals tend to avoid one another. Also they have, to some extent, different habits and habitats, or coexist under a sort of mutual respect for the fighting capabilities of each other.

Such an armed neutrality seems to exist between coyote and badger where the animals appear to be traveling together as friends.

Coyotes will sometimes kill foxes and bobcats they find alive in traps. Sperry's study of coyote food habits disclosed coyote meat in coyote stomachs, which probably was the remains of a trapped or dead animal.

Ravens and magpies, which feed mostly on carrion, feed under a sort of armed truce with coyotes. The coyote will often share a carcass with the birds, but only because the coyote cannot do much about it. He can chase the birds, but they fly or hop out of reach and immediately come back.

However, the coyote does gain some protection from association with these birds, especially with ravens. While the coyote is feeding on a carcass, ravens will be scattered around the area, some on the ground, some flying around or perched in high places. From these vantage points they see the approach of potential danger and by their alarm warn the coyote.

Coyotes can be quite sociable, which is typical of members of the dog family. Often small groups are seen together, but I am inclined to think that these are family groups for the most part. It may be that coyotes other than family members get together at times, but it is im-

Ravens are usually around to help a coyote clean up his meals.

This group was thought to be a family pack hunting together.

possible for an observer to determine this. A family is often indicated because of the difference in size between a female and her pups.

I once watched a group of five playing together on a snow-covered bench near the Gardiner River in north Yellowstone Park. They were all about the same size and I am quite sure they were litter mates. I saw eighteen coyotes within a short distance of a fresh kill in Yellowstone between Tower Falls and Cooke City. Most of these acted like singles, or nonrelated animals, and there was one rather vicious but short fight between six animals that were trying to get at the kill. The tendency of a coyote to spend its life within a short distance of its birthplace seems to support the idea that coyotes traveling together are apt to be part of the same family.

Anyone who has considered the coyote a cowardly animal has merely to read the long and varied list of individuals that have survived severe, painful, and crippling injuries to realize just how wrong he was. However, it is unscientific to use such terms as "cowardly" or "courageous" when describing a coyote or any other animal, for those are human terms that do not always apply correctly to wild creatures.

A female coyote killed near Tule Lake in northern California had four healthy pups in a den, though she herself was only in fair condition. She had been shot in both eyes with a shotgun and was blind. Would you consider her "brave"? It seems only that she must have had a tremendous will to survive—a trait common to people as well as to wild animals.

A cattle-ranching friend of mine, Carl Schnabele, has a good-sized spread of land in the rolling high desert country of eastern Oregon. Some years ago he and his son, Lester, bolstered the ranch income during the winter by doing a little coyote bounty hunting. They had two dogs that were good at the job. All that Carl and Lester had to do after the coyote had been killed was to get off their horses and cut off the dead coyote's ears, evidence needed to collect a bounty.

The World of the Coyote

One day when Carl stepped off his horse and reached for the ears of a downed coyote, he discovered it had none. Apparently, this one had been left for dead the previous year and its ears taken for the bounty. Fully recovered, it was getting along nicely despite the handicap.

Stories of three-legged coyotes are so plentiful that one could almost assume that losing one leg bothers a coyote not at all. A female Michigan coyote had only stubs of front legs and looked like a kangaroo when she ran. At the time she was killed, she was carrying five unborn young.

A trapped Colorado coyote was missing a left front and a right hind foot. However, the missing feet did not seem to hamper the animal's ability to make a living, for it was in fine physical condition when captured.

Another two-legged coyote, this time with the legs missing from the right side, was killed in New Mexico. It was a calf killer. It did not use the stumps when traveling but somehow managed to get around on the two left feet.

Healthy coyotes have been killed in which the lower jaws had previously been shot away or badly damaged. A predator control agent in Idaho captured a coyote that at one time had had its mouth cruelly wired shut. At the time of capture the hide had grown completely over the wire indicating that the wiring had taken place quite some time before. It was able to open its mouth only about a half inch, but, nevertheless, had been able to survive. These and similar reports bear witness to the fact that a coyote can adjust to severe physical disability.

Although American Indians used the fur of the coyote for wearing apparel, the early American fur traders paid little attention to their potential value until around 1860, when the supply of beaver skins began to fall off. Coyotes were referred to as "cased wolf," and the best prices were paid for prime skins. In the United States the best skins came from the Rocky Mountain States between October and early March.

Coyote fur is classed as "long fur" and is used mostly as trimming for coat collars and sleeves. Most coyote fur can be dyed black and, so dyed, has been sold as imitation black fox. Coyote fur has never been extremely popular, and the market for skins has been subject to much fluctuation. However, coyote fur coats had their period of glory when they were marketed as coonskin coats in the "sheik and flapper" era of the middle 1920's.

At the time (1925) $15.00 was paid for prime pelts taken from the vicinity of Fort Smith, Canada. Canadian coyote pelts generally brought higher prices. For the year ending March 31, 1944, the number of coyotes trapped in Alberta, Canada, was 31,028; their pelts brought a total of $508,618.08, or an average of $16.36 per pelt. For the years 1937–1942, North Dakota skins averaged only $7.22. In 1946, the Canadian fur auction sales held at Montreal, Canada, brought a top price of $16.00 a skin for the best of 1,100 coyotes offered. During the period 1933–1946, the highest average price on the Seattle fur exchange was $9.41 in 1947. The annual raw fur value of coyote pelts

Photographed in early January in ten-below-zero weather. This animal's coat was in prime condition.

The World of the Coyote

just before World War II was $1,000,000, but the 20 per cent luxury tax imposed by the Federal Government increased the cost of fur-trimmed coats beyond the means of the low- and middle-income class groups who buy most of them. When the demand for fur-trimmed coats dropped off, the demand for coyote pelts subsided.

Coyote fur has not been in demand for some time. The following are average prices paid for coyote pelts taken in Oregon as determined from the annual reports of licensed trappers to the Oregon State Game Commission. This represents only a small percentage of coyote pelts taken in the state as U. S. Fish and Wildlife Service trappers do not need a trapping license. However, the figures do show comparative market values for the fur.

Year	Average price	Year	Average price	Year	Average price
1941–42	$4.44	1949–50	$ .81	1957–58	$1.00
1942–43	5.64	1950–51	.73	1958–59	1.15
1943–44	8.55	1951–52	.40	1959–60	1.99
1944–45	3.26	1952–53	1.35	1960–61	2.23
1945–46	3.08	1953–54	.71	1961–62	2.11
1946–47	1.58	1954–55	.65	1962–63	2.63
1947–48	2.24	1955–56	1.42		
1948–49	.81	1956–57	1.12		

If we relate these prices to $15.00 a skin in 1925 and take into account the inflation of our currency between then and now, we see that present skins are bringing only a fraction of what they did in 1925. It is quite likely that the increased production and use of fur synthetics such as nylon, Acrilan, etc., will prevent less desirable furs from ever again becoming popular.

I am sure that few people these days are concerned with whether or not the coyote is an edible animal. Yet it is fairly certain that they were occasionally eaten by early Indians, and as white men moved westward, coyote may have often meant the difference between being

108

fed and starving. There are people in the world today who eat dogs, and there is no reason to assume that a coyote would not be equally palatable to them.

I have never eaten coyote nor have I ever talked to anyone who has. Ralph Sickles, a taxidermist in Bend, Oregon, told me of a friend that "would eat anything." He said he had tried coyote and found it "very tough and without much flavor." Several trappers I have talked with say they never have tried it and they weren't very enthusiastic about the idea.

I have read a report that said the meat of a coyote is comparable to that of the large gray wolf. Another report stated that the meat of a grown male coyote is as rank as that of an old billy goat.

The coyote's reputation as a killer of game and livestock has caused some fear that the animal constitutes a threat to the safety of campers or others who might be in coyote territory. There seems to be no basis for such a fear. I have never heard of a coyote deliberately attacking a human being. When trapped or otherwise cornered, it has been known to bite, but when given the chance it will run away rather than attack.

I had an experience several years ago during which I thought for a few anxious moments I was going to be the first person to be attacked by a coyote. I had heard of a coyote that had been raised from a pup on a high desert ranch in central Oregon. The thing that interested me most was that the animal had been raised with the farm dogs and had been allowed to grow up in complete freedom. I made arrangements to drive out and see this animal.

As I neared the ranch headquarters, I met the foreman heading out for the nearest settlement 30 miles away. I introduced myself. He had been expecting me. He pointed to a field where the coyote was romping with a slightly larger springer spaniel. I drove near the animals, got out, and began taking pictures of them. To improve the camera angle I knelt on the ground some 10 feet away.

The World of the Coyote

For the first time the coyote seemed to notice me. He stopped playing with the dog and came at me, his lips curled back, his wicked-looking canine teeth bared.

The coyote, a full-grown one, grabbed my arm between his jaws, just below my elbow. I braced myself for the shock, expecting him to crunch down, but he never did. I learned later that this was just a trick the animal had learned, and that he apparently had no intention of biting. He had never bitten anyone, and if it is possible that a coyote has a sense of humor, he may have enjoyed testing me. I was scared enough to run, but I couldn't get to my feet in time.

Lester Abbie told me of hungry coyotes getting quite bold in the winter around Mammoth in Yellowstone Park. At least one youngster returning from the grocery store was jumped on and bitten by a coyote, but this was to make her drop the sack of groceries she was carrying. The coyote then picked up all it could carry in its mouth and ran off, leaving the girl alone.

There are records of coyotes feeding on human bodies, but these were not people killed by the animals. Victor H. Cahalane states, "I have never heard of a normal coyote biting a human, unless it did so incidentally when reaching for food. It seems safe to say that a normal wild coyote will not attack a person."

Similarly J. Frank Dobie says: "I have never met a single account approaching authenticity of normal coyotes' attacking a live human being."

Some studies have been made of the migratory habits of coyotes by tagging and releasing. Much interesting information has been gained in this manner though it is inconclusive, showing rather wide variations, and some unexplainable movements. Their travels seem influenced by the scarcity or abundance of natural foods, livestock movements, and climate.

In New Mexico a small group of coyotes from the same area were tagged and released. From a tagged litter of 7 six- to eight-week-old pups, three were subsequently caught. One, captured a year and sixteen days after release, was over 100 miles from the release point. Another was captured 18 miles from release point two years later, and the third was only 5 miles from the release point nine years later. They were all male pups. Except for the one that was 100 miles away, all of the recaptures from New Mexico were within a few miles of the release point. This was in an area of abundant natural foods and no severe winter weather.

In a Wyoming study it appeared that coyote migrations were more influenced by weather and livestock movements. In general, coyotes moved down from high elevations of deep snow into lower areas and consistently followed herds of sheep as they moved to winter ranges at lower elevations.

Occasionally, an unbelievably long trip is made by a coyote such as the one marked near Phoenix, Arizona, and captured eight months later 250 miles away near the south rim of the Grand Canyon. It was assumed that the movement of this animal was influenced by the movement of sheep.

There seems to be no explanation for the coyote that evidently traveled all the way from Burns, Oregon, to Clearwater County, Idaho.

A coyote hunting.

The World of the Coyote

When captured, the animal was wearing a sheep bell with "H. H. Burns, Oregon" carved on the bell strap. It is approximately 400 air miles from Burns, Oregon, to the point of capture, and to get there, the coyote would have had to cross the mighty Snake River. Such a jaunt would prove the coyote's ability to extend its range some distance into new country.

Deep snows will force coyotes to migrate to lower elevations.

Winter

THE MIDDLE of the winter marks the beginning of the coyote's breeding season. Normally, the pregnant female carries her pups through the last of winter and the first of spring. Thus, a bad winter and low food supplies may bring about starvation for the female coyote carrying young, and the resultant litter may be considerably smaller than one born to a well-fed female.

There seems to be some question as to whether coyotes mate for life, though it is fairly well established that mated couples will stay together for several years. Ernest Thompson Seton reports: "It is the opinion of all persons familiar with its habits, that this animal, like the wolf, is strictly monogamous." Observations and studies made since those written by Mr. Seton (1909) generally bear out his statement. There are indications, however, that occasionally coyotes may be polygamous.

The breeding season is limited to less than two months for the female and to less than four months for the male. It most often starts around February 1 and lasts about a month. Whiteman reports that in a captive pair pro-oestrum lasted seventy-four days in a two-year-old female and oestrum* four days. Another female had a five-day oestrum.

* The period of sexual heat. The oestrous cycle is the period in mature females of many kinds of mammals when the desire of mating occurs. It varies in length, is controlled by hormones, and is often accompanied by bodily changes. The pro-oestrum is a preparatory period (preceding the oestrum) of increasing activity of the generative organs. The oestrum, or mating period, is the only time when the female is willing to mate and coition is fruitful.—EDITOR.

Hunting mice in a snow-covered meadow.

Early-born pups found in Oregon dens and hunters' estimates of their ages indicate an early January or late December breeding.

Victor H. Cahalane remarks: "With rare exceptions, if they [coyotes] do not find mates during that one period, the animals are unable to breed until the following year."

Finding mates should not be much of a problem, at least for the females, if this reported observation by Joseph Grinnell and his California associates is any indication: "A coyote, presumed to be a female, came in sight and to within ¼ and ½ mile of the house. Following the female was a line of scattered coyotes, apparently all males in a column 'at least 4 miles long,' as judged by the time it took to pass the house. In all, there were eleven animals, yapping loudly and going at a rapid pace—ten males in pursuit of the single female."

Stanley P. Young states that "there is evidence that females breed when a year old." However, Ernest Thompson Seton reported that coyotes were more likely to follow the same pattern as the larger wolves and not breed until two years old. Joseph Grinnell and his associates state that many females do not breed until they are nearly two years old.

One litter a year seems to be the rule for coyotes. As with most rules, there are exceptions. A female coyote caught near Bakersfield, California, showed plainly that she had been nursing a litter of young within the previous twenty-four hours. An autopsy of the dead animal disclosed that her body contained seven small embryos of a forthcoming second litter.

Eldon E. Whiteman, from his study of captive coyotes, concludes that "probably the coyote is monoestrous." Gestation period for coyotes is sixty to sixty-five days; Young says sixty to sixty-three days; Palmer, sixty-three days.

There are sufficient records available of coyote-dog breedings to indicate that the two species hybridize readily, either crossing male domestic dog with female coyote, or male coyote with female dog.

115

The offspring are fertile. The hybrids generally show characteristics of both parents, although the coyote tendency toward shyness often seems to predominate. "Coy-dog" hybrids do not have the natural affection for people that dogs do and will often show physical or character exaggerations when compared with either parent.

It appears that such crosses in the wild are infrequent. In some eastern states, where coyote populations have started by animals being imported from the West and then released, coyotes unable to find coyote mates have mated with domestic dogs.

In February, 1964, I was advised by the Connecticut Board of Fisheries and Game that all cases of coyotelike animals killed or observed within the state were labeled "coy-dogs" or coyote-dog crosses.

In a Montana experiment a female foxhound was bred to a male coyote. The offspring were all fighters but appeared more friendly than a full-blooded coyote. A female hybrid of this cross became a good trailer of bobcats and coyotes, and was an exceptionally good killer.

In the Royal Ontario Museum of Toronto, Ontario, Canada, there are two adult specimens, male and female, of a supposed coyote-wolf hybrid.

Coyotes are widely known as predators of livestock, game birds, and big-game mammals. It appears, however, that many people have an exaggerated idea of the extent of these predatory activities.

Game birds and big-game mammals form a regular though comparatively small part of the coyote's diet. A portion of this game is eaten as carrion whose death resulted from some cause other than a coyote's attack, but a considerable percentage is killed by coyotes. According to Charles C. Sperry's study, *Food Habits of the Coyote*, game birds and big-game mammals comprise approximately 4 to 5 per cent by volume of coyote diets. This includes deer at 3.58 per cent, antelope at .05 per cent, and all others together at about 1 per cent.

While these figures are low and would seem to indicate that coyote

116

predation on game birds and big-game mammals is insignificant, this might not be locally true. In certain restricted areas or for short periods of time coyotes might be doing considerable damage to game populations. Another pitfall that one can encounter by accepting such figures too quickly is that a small percentage of coyote food might actually represent a large percentage of the game population under certain conditions. Coyotes could consume much of a game species in a certain area and such game might still represent only a small part of the coyote's total food consumption. I do not mean that this is always true. Predation is only one of many things that help to keep all wildlife populations within bounds. Many factors must be taken into consideration to evaluate properly coyote predation.

There seem to be widely varying opinions about coyote-deer relationships. Some feel that coyotes prey extensively on all deer including full-grown healthy ones. Others seem convinced that coyotes get only a few deer and these generally the small, inferior, or diseased animals. Most Federal trappers with whom I have talked consider predation more serious than do most game management personnel, who tend to look at it as a minor factor in game losses.*

Adolph Murie, in his study of the coyote in Yellowstone, states: "Behavior of adult deer when in proximity to coyotes shows that they are not afraid, but on the contrary are prone to assume the offensive. There was no indication that healthy adult deer were killed. Bucks generally pay little attention to coyotes, but does usually are more attentive and seem somewhat concerned, and their behavior suggests that they recognize the coyote as a potential enemy to their fawns . . . . Observations indicate, then, that at times deer chase coyotes, and at other times coyotes chase deer and prey on certain individuals. . . . The coyote is by no means able to kill deer at will."

* Probably because their jobs and living depend on their continued employment as trappers, wildlife management personnel, trained as scientists, are more reliable judges of the role of predation.—EDITOR.

The World of the Coyote

These observations agree pretty much with my own made during winter trips into Yellowstone. During the first, in February, 1958, I watched a pack of five coyotes playing just over a hill, only about 50 yards beyond a group of deer bedded down in the snow. From my observation point, which was quite a bit higher than the animals, the direction of the wind was from the coyotes to the deer, but it may have been different down where they were. The deer gave no indication of concern, and I was forced to conclude that the deer either were not afraid or did not know the coyotes were there.

On another trip in January, 1964, I watched a small herd of antelope. They were feeding on the scanty vegetation protruding through 6 to 8 inches of snow and moved slowly past a coyote perched on a knoll and looking for something to eat. Scattered about in the brushy draws nearby were a half-dozen more coyotes.

Coyotes had been trotting all over the area and I am sure the antelope could scent them, but they continued their leisurely feeding.

Victor H. Cahalane reports an experience which illustrates that not all deer are afraid of coyotes. A yearling doe was pursued to the top

Coyotes have little success hunting strong, healthy mule deer bucks like this one.

Unless one of these antelopes could be separated from the herd, a coyote could not do much with them.

The young antelope trailing the two mature antelope bucks would be easy prey for a coyote, but it would first have to separate the youngster from the two mature buck antelopes.

of a slope by a single coyote. She then turned downhill and on the downhill run was intercepted by two more coyotes. At the bottom of the slope, the coyotes attacked and brought her down. The cries of the mortally wounded yearling attracted seven other deer—six does and a fawn. They kept moving closer until the largest doe lunged into the coyote pack and struck out with her front hooves together. The big doe kept up its attack for some time but finally gave up and left.

After the yearling died, the three coyotes started quarreling over the carcass. One drove off the other two which were able to feed only after the dominant coyote would permit it.

John F. Aiton states in his "Relationship of Predators to Whitetail Deer in Glacier National Park": "The small percentage of the losses attributable to predators in comparison to the large percentage due to other causes definitely places the predator problem in a secondary status. The overcrowding of the winter range of the whitetailed deer, resulting in an inferior and decreased forage supply, presents a problem of primary importance. In this instance, 138 out of 240, or 57.5 per cent of the dead deer examined were found not to have been killed by coyotes."

Fawns probably bear the brunt of coyote predation. In the spring, they are quite tiny and if coyotes can find them and can avoid the mother, they are easy prey. During the winter and early spring, fawns have tough going finding food in deep snows and are the first to weaken from lack of food. Adolph Murie states: "The coyotes were probably preying upon fawns which, for the most part, were doomed to die from malnutrition or disease sooner or later during the winter. As pointed out elsewhere, several fawns were seen in an extremely weak condition. The ease with which I ran down a weak fawn suggests coyotes have no difficulty in securing a fawn in such condition and that very likely bands are followed by coyotes in order to pick up such weaklings. If all the fawns in a band happen to be strong, the coyotes probably seek food elsewhere. If deer in good condition were

120

not able to ward off a coyote attack, the relatively high survival of fawns often found in the midst of large populations of coyotes would not exist."

If there is one big-game animal whose numbers actually suffer from coyote predation, it is the antelope. The case against the brush wolf is not conclusive, but it seems that an overabundance of coyotes will keep small antelope herds from increasing. The situation in Oregon may be a case in point, though it is difficult to make positive determinations.

Since World War II, Oregon's antelope herds have not shown the growth that was expected. Hunting seasons have been held on an extremely limited basis, and the Game Commission has made extensive efforts to get accurate herd and fawn counts. Fawn counts in relation to hunter harvests indicate that the herds should be increasing, but they are not. One elaborate study several years ago involving the capture of several antelope fawns and a careful supervision of their diets to maturity brought only negative results. Nothing in what they were eating or the way they were eating accounted for the lack of herd increase. Best guess still seems to be that bobcats and coyotes are limiting the antelope population.

Paul V. Jones, Jr., writing in *Texas Game and Fish,* states: "Elimination of other factors indicates predation by coyotes on antelope fawns is the chief limiting factor operating to prevent the increase of antelope in the Upper and Lower Plains."

Coyote predation on game birds is quite minor on an over-all, year-round basis but can be severe in restricted areas or for short periods of time. Most of the damage is done to grouse and quail during the nesting season which, unfortunately, also coincides with the coyote whelping season. In southwestern Texas there was heavy coyote predation on early quail nests, but by midsummer it was comparatively light. Predation was not always proportional to nesting activities.

It is quite likely that sage grouse suffer more from coyote attack than any other bird. Their habitat is open sagebrush country which is in the coyote's home grounds. Sage grouse are big birds and have a habit of walking into waterholes each evening. A waiting coyote would have little trouble catching one as it walks by.

Prior to the white man's explorations of the West, coyotes ranged almost entirely on the flat arid plains west of the Mississippi River.

It was quite likely at that time that coyote populations fluctuated with the changes in the natural food supply or with the effects of disease epidemics. Great numbers of coyotes must have followed the vast buffalo herds and fed on the old and diseased that dropped behind or subsisted on the remains of those killed by wolves.

Then the buffalo hunters came. The herds were destroyed and, along with them, a big source of coyote food. Ranchers and homesteaders with poultry and livestock began to settle the land. The coyote quickly

During nesting season quail are occasionally hit pretty hard by coyotes.

discovered that, compared with deer and antelope, sheep and goats were easy to capture and kill. Ducks and chickens were also there for the taking.

As far back as the 1890's it was officially reported in Texas that "the greatest and most discouraging obstacle encountered by the sheepmen of Texas is that omnipresent evil, the depredations of wild animals."

Since these first clashes between the farmer-rancher and the coyote, there has been continuous war.

In general, livestock seems to actually represent only a minute portion of total coyote food. This does not obviate the fact that in certain restricted areas, at certain times of the year, livestock predation by coyotes can be a big factor. In some areas feral dogs cause damage to livestock, although coyotes usually get the blame. In the twelve-month period ending June 30, 1963, 800 feral dogs were destroyed in one Willamette Valley county in Oregon.

Sheep and goats are most susceptible to coyote attack, but some calves are killed and, occasionally, an adult cow. However, the size of most horses, cattle, and pigs, along with their protective capabilities, make it difficult for a coyote to kill them.

In the spring of 1963, coyotes were reported to have killed some 100 calves in Benton County, Washington. One rancher said the marauding coyotes were so bold that he could get close enough to hit them with sticks and stones and that one of his hired hands had to use a pitchfork to drive coyotes away from a new-born calf.

During the winter of 1962–1963, coyotes in eastern Oregon were believed to have killed a cow and her calf after forcing them out onto ice. In another incident they were believed to have killed a calf and then caused the cow to fall off a rimrock. The injured cow was later killed by the coyotes.

Adolph Murie in his study, "Coyote Food Habits on a Southwestern Cattle Range," states: "Most of the cattle consumed was carrion, but there was some predation on calves. Among the purebred Herefords

A coyote comes in for an attack on a calf.

Suddenly aware of the danger, the calf starts to run.

The calf's mother routs the attacking coyote.

kept on good range it was known that predation was insignificant. On the overstocked ranges most types of losses were large. Although coyote predation here appeared to be light, no accurate measurement of the loss due to coyotes was possible. Some calves that were weak, too weak to follow the cows, were killed by coyotes."

Since the early days many big livestock damage bills have been charged against the coyote. There seems little doubt that until extensive efforts to control the coyote populations were undertaken, these animals did considerable damage to sheep and goat herds and, in some cases, wiped them out entirely. However, in recent years, with constant control of the animal and continuing studies of coyotes and their relationship to livestock and game, new and more accurate evaluations of the coyote's place in our economy are being made.

H. T. Gier, reporting on coyotes in Kansas, states: "Coyote damage in Kansas was about $1,350,000 in 1949. Chief damage was to chickens, calves, and sheep. Poultry and livestock losses appeared to be roughly inversely proportionate to availability of rabbits and rodents. Benefits from coyotes would be greater than losses except for individual 'killers.' When rabbits and rodents were plentiful, about 60 per cent of females bred and had litters that averaged six or more. When rabbits and rodents were scarce, as few as 30 per cent of females bred and had litters of about four."

In Utah, of 64,000 sheep pastured in a 250-square-mile area, 186 were lost to coyotes in a five-month period. This represents a loss rate of less than 1 per cent a year. Losses from other sources were two and a half times the losses to coyotes.

In one California county 448 goats were lost to coyotes in a two-year period, and there was evidence that a great part of the killing was done by one crippled, trap-shy coyote.

A study of the food habits of peg-leg coyotes disclosed that crippled animals will consume about 50 per cent more livestock than a normal coyote. In many instances of extensive predation on livestock within

125

a limited area, it has been found that most of the damage can be attributed to either a crippled animal or an old and weak one. These animals, no longer physically able to catch and kill wild species, concentrate on the easy way to obtain sheep, goats, and poultry.

It has been suggested that an inexperienced and clumsy trapper could reduce the coyote population in a given area by 50 per cent and, at the same time, create a worse predator problem than was there before he started. Poor trapping techniques allow coyotes to escape and increases the number of peg-leg animals. Even if an animal escapes the trap without serious injury, it will be trap-shy in the future.

Beginning in the late 1850's and continuing for the next twenty-five years, the coyote was subjected to the greatest mass poisoning ever instituted by man. The program was widespread, and many thousands were taken around the strychnine-poisoned carcasses of buffalo and antelope. However, they were being taken for their pelts rather than because of their predations.

Around 1885 poisoners went out of business either because the price of coyote pelts was too low, or the numbers of coyotes were depleted to such an extent that it was no longer profitable. With the coyote's capacity to reproduce, it did not take the population long to build up again.

With the bison herds gone and antelope greatly depleted, coyotes turned to livestock, which stirred men to begin a new war of extermination against them. Tremendous campaigns have been waged against coyotes, and unbelievable numbers have been killed. During the thirty-year period between July 1, 1915, and June 30, 1946, Federal control operations accounted for the destruction of 1,780,915 coyotes. Undoubtedly, hundreds of thousands more were killed and not reported during this period by men not employed by the government.

During the eighteen-year period ending June 30, 1963, Federal predator control activities accounted for 92,581 coyotes in the state of Oregon alone. If Oregon is representative of the western states, coyotes are being killed at the greatest rate since the days of the "wolf poisoner," possibly even faster. However, these figures do not necessarily mean that the amount of control is actually exterminating coyotes. We seem to have about as many in Oregon as there has been at any time in the last twenty years. In fact, some of the predator control men with whom I have talked seem to feel that coyote populations are increasing and that control measures should be intensified.

W. Robert Eadie reports that for one year, ending June 30, 1950, a total of 294,000 coyotes were taken by a combination of supervised and unsupervised hunters. "It has been suggested that this large harvest represents only the annual increase in the coyote populations."

Along its runway the coyote establishes "scent posts."

The World of the Coyote

Many ranchers, instead of killing coyotes or warring against them, actually try to protect them on rangelands of the West. In 1953, ranchers in the vicinity of Toponas, Colorado, members of the Toponas Grassland Protective Association, posted their lands against the killing of coyotes. They also opposed the widespread destruction of weasels, hawks, eagles, skunks, foxes, and other predatory animals that help to keep rodent populations under control, or in check.

Mr. E. C. Shindorf, Chairman of the Board of Directors of the Toponas Grassland Protective Association, wrote an article "Coyotes Protected" (*Audubon Magazine*, September-October, 1953, issue), asserting that:

"The reason for this attitude is that for 10 years or so we have watched the steady increase of mice, gophers, moles, rabbits, and other rodents. Now we are at a point where these animals take up to one-third of our hay crop and have cut the carrying capacity of livestock on our range lands by as much as one-half. . . .

"What with government hunters and government poison, the predators have had a hard time. The coyote is nearly extinct in our part of the state. Foxes and bobcats have succumbed to the chain-killing poisons. There are fewer hawks and eagles every year, and weasels . . . are very scarce. It is little wonder we have so many rodents.

"The Toponas Grassland Protective Association has been formed to take action in this crisis. We strongly oppose the use of chain-killing methods for control of any animal. By this we mean use of any poison whereby another animal will suffer the lethal effects from coming in contact with, or eating the carrion or exudations from, an animal which has died as a result of consuming an initial poison dosage.

"In view of this policy, our association vigorously opposes the use of 1080 poison in any form in the state of Colorado. Believing that 1080 poison is an extremely dangerous and deadly chain killer which constitutes the greatest menace to our natural predators, we advocate the outlawing of this poison, as well as thalium and cyanide guns, in Colorado.

"Our association now represents more than 200,000 acres of land in this area. This means that on at least that much territory coyotes and most other predators are to have a chance to live without persecution and to increase in numbers so that they can once again play the role that nature intended, and be an effective check on the rodent population."

The use of steel traps is one of the oldest methods of catching wild animals and is the one most in use today. Many persons consider them inhumane, and no doubt the suffering, trapped animals would agree. Unfortunately, there is no better or more practical device to take their place. However, the steel trap is only as good as the trapper who sets it, and one improperly placed will catch little, if anything.

As coyotes travel the range along their runways, they establish "scent posts," at intervals. These are places where they stop to urinate. Each time a coyote goes by one of these, he stops and urinates. Strange coyotes coming through the area will also leave their "calling cards" there.

The area around a scent post is a potentially successful place for a trap. If a trapper is unable to find a natural scent post, he makes one by using a strong scent of which coyote urine is the base. Several traps may be set in the area, but great care must be exercised in setting them because a coyote is a wise animal. In order not to be contaminated with "man" smell, traps are buried under a thin layer of soil. Some traps are staked to the ground; others are fastened to a drag.

Trapper Art Cooper had an interesting experience with a trapped coyote. The animal, which had been killing sheep, was finally caught in a two-trap set, both of which were fastened to an iron drag. The coyote was caught in both traps, one on a front foot and one on a hind foot. When Cooper and a companion came upon the animal, it was trying to cross a plowed field. It was having a lot of trouble because the drag kept tripping it up. Finally, the coyote grabbed the drag in its mouth and then was able to make good speed.

The World of the Coyote

Finding coyote dens and destroying the pups is considered one of the most effective methods to limit the increase of coyotes. Also, at denning time one or both of the parents may be seen around the den, giving the hunter an opportunity for a shot. Dens are not easy to locate and it usually costs an experienced hunter a lot of time and a lot of looking to find one. Tracks of the parent animals after the pups are born will often point toward the den. When hunting, the coyote will meander around as it looks for food. Once it has made a kill, it will head straight toward the den. Eventually tracks leading to the den will radiate out from it like the spokes of a wheel.

The use of poison for predator control has always been highly controversial, possibly because it can so easily be misused and because poison does not discriminate between its victims. In the past, strychnine was widely used, but in recent years a new poison, Compound 1080, has been developed. Compound 1080 is an extremely effective weapon against predators, but it has many drawbacks. It is very poisonous to man, beast and bird. The effects may carry through several hosts with lethal results, and there is no known antidote.

One of the most ancient methods of predator control is the bounty system which seems to date back about 2,700 years. It got an early start in this country in Massachusetts in 1630. Almost as soon as man moved into coyote country, he established a bounty on the animals. Substantially all present-day students of predator control agree that bounties achieve few if any of the intended results. In fact, bounties may actually result in an increase in the number of the very predators they are supposed to eliminate.

As soon as killing predators becomes a source of income, it becomes obvious that to perpetuate the income one must perpetuate the source. Bounty hunters operate in areas where they can get the most with the least effort, and these may not necessarily be the animals that are doing the damage. Fraudulent claims have been made and collected amounting to hundreds of thousands of dollars for pelts that were not what

130

they were stated to be, or were not from the state paying the bounty. Often, trapped females were released in order to perpetuate the animals, and there are records of hunters getting pups from dens and raising them in captivity for the higher bounties paid for adult animals.

In one section where tails were acceptable evidence for bounty collection, the tails of trapped females would be cut off and the animals released to continue on their productive way.

In Oregon it was found that the greatest number of bountied animals came during big-game hunting seasons when many hunters were in the woods. This indicates that these were animals that would have been killed anyway and were only brought in because a bounty would be paid. Because of these and other reasons, most states have discontinued the bounty system.

If there must be predator control, the use of Federal hunter-trappers appears to be most efficient and economical.

Probably more coyotes are shot incidental to deer and antelope hunting than any other way. During the hunting season, offal from slain deer and antelopes, plus hunter-crippled animals, provides easy pickings for coyotes. But with the woods full of hunters, many of whom stay motionless much of the time, it is almost impossible for a coyote to stay out of sight of everyone. Most hunters look upon coyotes as harmful predators and are convinced that each one killed adds that many more deer to the herds. They take a shot at every one they see.

However, some hunters will hunt coyotes in the same manner as they hunt deer. That is, they go into coyote country armed with high-velocity, small-bore rifles and look for them.

Coyote hunting has never been highly popular as a sport. Probably the oldest method is to use fast dogs to run them down. These may be greyhounds, Russian wolfhounds, or Scottish deerhounds, or crossbreeds of these. While there are undoubtedly many ways of hunting with hounds, also called "coursing," it basically involves sighting a

The World of the Coyote

coyote, then turning the dogs loose to run it down. These dogs are "sight runners" as compared with foxhounds or beagles that trail by scent. Frequently the coyotes are chased by automobiles until the hunters are within striking distance of the animals, and then the hounds are turned loose.

Because this kind of coyote hunting is limited to flat open plains country and to hunters with dogs, it has relatively few participants.

Only in recent years have predator calls gained in popularity, although their effectiveness has long been well known. Quite likely the Indians were calling coyotes and other animals into bow and arrow range long before white men came to this continent.

All predator calls do about the same thing. They imitate the distress call of a rabbit in trouble. To a listening coyote this means a free meal. Unless something has made it suspicious, it will come running. Foxes also will answer the call, sometimes more readily than a coyote. A bobcat can also be lured by the call.

If coyotes are going to answer a call, most of them will come quickly.

Coyotes and Man

MUCH HAS been said about the coyote as a shy, retiring animal, but observations have indicated that much of this shyness is shrewdly calculated and is based on the potential danger to the animal. It is my opinion that coyotes must be classified as one of the smartest species on the North American continent. This characteristic seems amply evidenced by the animal's successful relationship with advancing civilization.

In each of my last five trips to Yellowstone, I have observed coyotes which have learned that tourists provide a good source of food, and they station themselves along the road for their handouts. I spent several hours watching one in the fall of 1963. Its actions were more or less typical of other "begging" coyotes I have seen. The animal had its regular beat, a stretch of road about 200 yards long, which included a picnic table turn-out. I suspect that finding scraps around this table might have had some influence on the coyote becoming a beggar.

At that particular time of the year, late September, the coyote was only on its beat during the afternoons. This seemed strange, at first, until I realized that at that time of the year, with overnight accommodations in the Park closed for the season, tourists would have to drive many miles from any entrance before arriving at this coyote's begging spot. Consequently, few people were there in the morning, and the animal had learned that there was no reward for being there at that time.

The animal was cautious, but not afraid, and would approach within

10 feet to take food thrown to him. This is about as close as I have seen any of these coyotes come to a person.

I have frequently observed coyotes on the outskirts of the small towns around central Oregon. Some may even come into the towns, but I have not heard of it. However, there is much wild country in that part of Oregon. Seeing coyotes there is not as meaningful as the fact that there are some living in the Hollywood hills in southern California. They have been seen drinking out of swimming pools and enjoying lawn sprinklers. Occasionally, one gets flattened on a freeway, and they have been heard howling in the nearby hills. In a two-year period one trapper is reported to have taken fifty-eight coyotes within fifteen minutes' driving distance of the center of Hollywood.

For quite some time a coyote lived on the Amarillo, Texas, airport. The animal was under constant observation from the weather tower, and when planes came in for a landing, it would move off to one side of the runway and watch the aircraft. There were apparently enough rabbits on the airfield to keep it well fed.

For a good many years, the coyote was considered a villain, and all efforts were aimed at its extermination. In more recent years this thinking has changed somewhat, and much serious thought and research are being devoted to determining accurately just where and how the coyote fits into modern man's civilization.

Numerous evaluations of the coyote have been made: as a costly predator of livestock and game, compared with its value in rodent control; as a scavenger; as a trophy for hunters; as a fascinating part of our native fauna that should be preserved; or as a tourist attraction in the West, especially in the national parks. It is easy to find arguments for each of these views. What do some of the authorities say about it?

Dr. E. Raymond Hall, a scientist and Director of the Museum of Natural History, University of Kansas, states: "He is a health officer among game and other animals, including man himself. For one thing, he is a scavenger, and on watersheds, which supply water for domestic use, he retrieves many a carcass for food that otherwise would decay and contaminate the water supply, or serve as a lure to filth-loving insects which carry the organisms of decay to man's food."

It is generally accepted that the coyote preys on the weak and sickly members of our game birds and big-game mammals, and thus is beneficial to the health of game populations. However, I have been told by every predator trapper with whom I have talked that they kill many more game animals than is generally known, and furthermore, that they do not confine their predations to diseased or weak animals. Contrasted to the trappers' views are the studies of animal ecologists who have demonstrated the natural function and necessity of predators in keeping animal populations within the limits of their food supplies.

Adolph Murie remarked on this problem as follows: "This attitude toward predatory animals is easily understood, for one kill or an apparent kill makes a striking impression on the mind. The attention is held by an individual instance rather than by the effect of predation on the entire population."

While coyotes may not control rodent populations, they do feed extensively on them and have a suppressive effect that is useful, as all predation seems to be. Major population fluctuations of rodents, however, seem not affected by the number of coyotes around. Jack rabbits, ground squirrels, and other rodents have a high reproductive potential which, under favorable conditions, may get far beyond control by coyotes, even where they are present in abundance. However, the predations of hawks, owls, weasels, foxes, and other animals added to predation of coyotes have a cumulative effect in rodent suppression.

It appears that more and more of the contemporary game experts lean toward the concept that predator populations have little significant effect on game populations. The most important effects on game populations are available food supplies, cover for protection, weather, and other natural factors.

Coyote predation on livestock is more of a problem. However,

The World of the Coyote

damage usually occurs in comparatively confined areas and is caused by a relatively few individuals.

As W. Robert Eadie puts it: "From all these studies of the coyote there emerges the realistic view that the status of the coyote as a predator is always a local problem."

The coyote is controversial, is one of the few animals to hold its own with man, and has been able to extend its range in spite of the encroachments of civilization; all these reasons make it one of the most interesting species we have in this country. Symbol of the plains and prairies of the West, the coyote is a part of our traditions and deserves a permanent place with us as a long-tested and successful member of our American fauna.

A begging coyote that was encountered in Yellowstone Park.

Coyote Subspecies

SCIENTIFICALLY, the coyote is classified in the phylum Chordata because it has a backbone. It is classed as a mammal because it is warm-blooded, has a four-chambered heart, hair on its body, gives birth to its young alive, and has mammary glands with which to nurse the young. It is in the order Carnivora because it is a flesh eater; it is in the family Canidae, with its brothers the foxes, wolves, and dogs. It is of the genus *Canis*, of which the native species of the genus on this continent are *Canis latrans*, the coyote; *Canis lupus*, the gray wolf; and *Canis niger*, the red wolf.

The following information on races, or subspecies, of coyotes and their approximate range has been taken from *The Mammals of North America* by E. Raymond Hall and Keith R. Kelson.

Canis latrans latrans. Plains coyote. Range: In Canada, southeastern Alberta, southern Saskatchewan, and the extreme southwestern corner of Manitoba; in the United States, Montana, Wyoming, and Colorado east of the Rocky Mountains, and the northeastern corner of New Mexico; North Dakota except northeastern quarter; northwestern Oklahoma, and northern Panhandle region of Texas.

Canis latrans incolatus. Northern coyote. Range: In Canada, Yukon Territory, Northwest Territory, northern British Columbia, and northern Alberta; in the United States, most of Alaska except the southeastern coastal sections.

Canis latrans thamnos. Northeastern coyote. Range: In Canada, north-central Saskatchewan, Manitoba, except extreme southwestern

137

Mountain coyote on May 1.

Mountain coyote on October 1.

Mountain coyote on June 5. Note difference in pelage on this and the specimens in the previous two photographs.

corner, southern Ontario, and extreme southern Quebec; in the United States, eastern edge of North Dakota, Minnesota, Iowa, Missouri, north of Missouri River; Michigan, Wisconsin, Illinois, except for extreme southern portion, and northern Indiana.

Canis latrans frustror. Southeastern coyote. Range: Extreme eastern and southeastern Kansas; eastern Oklahoma, eastern Texas, Missouri south of Missouri River except for southeastern corner; extreme west and northwest Arkansas.

Canis latrans texensis. Texas Plains coyote. Range: Texas, except for northern Panhandle region, eastern part, and extreme southern tip; eastern New Mexico except for northeastern corner; and part of northeastern Mexico.

Canis latrans lestes. Mountain coyote. Range: In Canada, southern British Columbia and southeastern Alberta; in the United States, Oregon and Washington east of the Cascade Mountains, northern California, Idaho, western Montana, Wyoming, and Colorado, except southeast corner; northern and central Nevada and northern and central Utah.

Canis latrans umpquensis. Northwest Coast coyote. Range: West of the Cascade Range in Oregon and Washington.

Canis latrans ochropus. California Valley coyote. Range: California west of the high Sierra Nevada mountains, except in the northern part.

Canis latrans clepticus. San Pedro Martir coyote. Range: Northern Baja California and southwestern California.

Canis latrans peninsulae. Peninsula coyote. Range: Baja California peninsula.

Canis latrans mearnsi. Mearns coyote. Range: Southwestern Colorado, extreme southern Utah and Nevada, southeastern California, northeastern Baja California, Arizona, New Mexico, west of Rio Grande, Sonora and Chihuahua in Mexico.

Canis latrans jamesi. Tiburon Island coyote. Range: Tiburon Island, Baja California.

Canis latrans microdon. Lower Rio Grande coyote. Range: Extreme southern Texas and northern Tamaulipas, Mexico.

Canis latrans impavidus. Durango coyote. Range: In Mexico, southern Sonora, southwestern Chihuahua, western Durango, western Zacatecas, and Sinaloa.

Canis latrans cagottis. Mexican coyote. Range: South central Mexico including Oaxaca, San Luis Potosí, Pueblo, and Veracruz.

Canis latrans vigilis. Colima coyote. Range: Southwestern Pacific slope of Jalisco, Michoacán, and Guerrero in Mexico.

Canis latrans goldmani. Chiapas coyote. Range: Western Guatemala.

Canis latrans dickeyi. Salvador coyote. Range: Costa Rica, Salvador, and Nicaragua.

Canis latrans hondurensis. Honduras coyote. Range: Honduras.

140

Reading References

Aiton, John F., "Relationship of Predators to Whitetail Deer in Glacier National Park." *Transactions of the Third North American Wildlife Conference.* Washington, American Wildlife Institute, 1938.

Alcon, J. R., "On the Decoying of Coyotes." *Journal of Mammalogy,* 27:122 (1946).

Almirall, Leon V., "Coursing Colorado Coyotes." *Travel,* Vol. 85, No. 1 (May, 1945), pp. 26–27, 32.

Arrington, O. N., and Edwards, Alfred E., "Predator Control as a Factor in Antelope Management." *Transactions of the Sixteenth North American Wildlife Conference,* pp. 179–193. Washington, Wildlife Management Institute, 1951.

Bailey, Bernard, "Mammals of Sherburne County, Minnesota." *Journal of Mammalogy,* 10:153 (1929).

Baily, Vernon, *The Mammals and Life Zones of Oregon.* U.S. Department of Agriculture, 1936.

Bryant, Harold C., "The Coyote Not Afraid of Water." *Journal of Mammalogy,* 1:87 (1920).

Buckley, John L., "Animal Population Fluctuations in Alaska—a History." *Transactions of the Nineteenth North American Wildlife Conference.* Washington, Wildlife Management Institute, 1954.

Burt, W. H., and Grossenheider, R. P., *A Field Guide to the Mammals.* Boston, Houghton Mifflin Company, 1952.

Cahalane, Victor H., "A Deer-Coyote Episode." *Journal of Mammalogy,* 28:36 (1947).

Cahalane, Victor H., *Mammals of North America.* New York, The Ronald Press Company, 1962.

Cates, E. C., "A Dilemma in Nature—Coyotes or Rodents." *South Dakota Conservation Digest,* Vol. 22, No. 7 (July, 1955), pp. 5–6, 10.

Clark, Ella E., *Indian Legends of the Pacific Northwest.* Berkeley, University of California Press, 1953.

Cockrum, E. Lendell, *Introduction to Mammalogy*. New York, The Ronald Press Company, 1962.

Colbert, Edwin H., *Evolution of the Vertebrates*. New York, John Wiley & Sons, Inc., 1955.

Compton, Horace O., "Effects of Predation on Pronghorn Antelope Numbers in South Central Oregon." Unpublished Master's thesis, Oregon State University, 1958.

Couch, Leo K., "Relationship of Predatory Mammals and Birds of Prey to Rodent Life." *Journal of Mammalogy*, 9:73 (1928).

Curtis, William, "The Coyote." *Outdoor Life*, Vol. 129, No. 6 (June, 1962), pp. 42–43, 152–155.

Dalrymple, Bryon W., "Mr. Slick the Coyote." *Sports Afield*, Vol. 150, No. 2 (August, 1963), pp. 53, 81–82.

Dice, Lee Raymond, "Notes on Some Mammals of Riley County, Kansas." *Journal of Mammalogy*. 4:108 (1923).

Dixon, Joseph, "Rodent and Reclamation in the Imperial Valley." *Journal of Mammalogy*, 3:137 (1922).

Dixon, Joseph, "Food Predilections of Predatory and Fur-Bearing Animals." *Journal of Mammalogy*, 6:34 (1925).

Dobie, J. Frank, *The Voice of the Coyote*, Boston, Little, Brown & Co., 1949.

Eadie, W. Robert, *Animal Control in Field, Farm and Forest*. New York, The Macmillan Company, 1954.

Ferrel, Carol M., Leach, Howard R., and Tillotson, Daniel F., "Food Habits of the Coyote in California." *California Fish and Game*, Vol. 39, No. 3 (July, 1953), pp. 301–341.

Fichter, Edson, "Watching Coyotes." *Journal of Mammalogy*, 31:66 (1950).

Finley, William L. and Irene, "Skeezix, a White Coyote." *Nature Magazine*, Vol. 15, No. 4 (April, 1930), pp. 227–229.

Gale, Larry R., and Pierce, Robert A., "Occurrence of the Coyote in Kentucky." *Journal of Mammalogy*, 35:256 (1954).

Gier, H. T., "Coyotes in Kansas." Manhattan, Agricultural Experiment Station, Bulletin 393, 1957.

Goldman, E. A., "The Predatory Mammal Problem and the Balance of Nature. *Journal of Mammalogy*, 6:28 (1925).

Green, D. D., "Albino Coyotes are Rare." *Journal of Mammalogy*, 28:63 (1947).

Grimm, Rudolf L., "Trout and Crayfish Eaten by Coyotes." *Journal of Mammalogy*, 21:458 (1940).

Bibliography

Grinnell, George Bird, "Eagles' Prey." *Journal of Mammalogy*, 10:83 (1929).

Grinnell, Joseph, Dixon, Joseph, and Linsdale, Jean M., *Fur Bearing Mammals of California*. Berkeley, University of California Press, 1937.

Hall, E. Raymond, "The Coyote and His Control." *California Fish and Game*, Vol. 17, No. 3 (July, 1931), pp. 283–290.

Hall, E. Raymond, and Kelson, Keith R., *The Mammals of North America*. New York, The Ronald Press Company, 1959.

Hansen, G. H., "Predator Control." *Oregon State Game Commission Bulletin*, Vol. 9, No. 11 (November, 1954), pp. 3–4.

Hanson, William R., and McCulloch, Clay Y., "Factors Influencing Mule Deer on Arizona Brushlands." *Transactions of the Twentieth North American Wildlife Conference*, pp. 568–588. Washington, Wildlife Management Institute, 1955.

Henderson, F. Robert, "Make Like A Rabbit." *Outdoor Life*, Vol. 129, No. 4 (April, 1962), pp. 76–78, 137–141.

Henderson, W. C., "The Control of the Coyote." *Journal of Mammalogy*, 11:336 (1930).

Horn, E. E., "Coyote-Wildlife Relationships." *Transactions of the Sixth North American Wildlife Conference*. Washington, American Wildlife Institute, 1941.

Howell, A. Brazier, "A Coyote Surviving Under Difficulties." *Journal of Mammalogy*, 9:63 (1928).

Jackson, Hartley H. T., "A Coyote in Maryland." *Journal of Mammalogy*, 3:186 (1922).

Jackson, Hartley H. T., *Mammals of Wisconsin*. Madison, The University of Wisconsin Press, 1961.

Jaeger, Edmund C., "The Coyote as a Seed Distributor." *Journal of Mammalogy*, 31:452 (1950).

Johnson, Jerry, "Coyote and Bull Snake." *Journal of Mammalogy*, 17:169 (1936).

Jones, Paul V., Jr., "Antelope Management." *Texas Game and Fish*, Vol. 7, No. 12 (November, 1949), pp. 4–5, 18–20, 24–25, 28–29.

Kebbe, Chester E., "The Bounty System in Oregon." *Oregon State Game Commission Bulletin*, Vol. 13, No. 11 (November, 1958), pp. 3–4.

Keller, L. Floyd, "Porcupines Killed and Eaten by a Coyote." *Journal of Mammalogy*, 16:232 (1935).

Korschgen, Leroy J., "Food Habits of the Coyote in Missouri." *Journal of Wildlife Management*, 21:424 (1957).

Lauckart, J. Burton, "Predator Management." Unpublished paper read before Conference of Western Association of State Game and Fish Commissioners, Santa Fe, N. M., June 13, 1961.

Lehman, Valgene W., "Bobwhite Quail Reproduction in Southwestern Texas." *Journal of Wildlife Management,* 10:111 (1946).

Loftin, Horace, "Nature Ramblings." *Science News Letter,* Vol. 77, No. 17 (April, 1960), p. 270.

Moore, Robert D., "*Canis latrans lestes* (Merriam) Feeding on Tadpoles and Frogs." *Journal of Mammalogy,* 10:255 (1929).

Murie, Adolph, *Ecology of the Coyote in the Yellowstone.* Washington, United States Department of the Interior, 1940.

Murie, Adolph, "Coyote Food Habits on a Southwestern Cattle Range." *Journal of Mammalogy,* 32:291 (1951).

Palmer, Ralph S., *The Mammal Guide.* Garden City, Doubleday & Company, Inc., 1954.

Presnall, Clifford C., and Wood, Alvin, "Coyote Predation on Sage Grouse." *Journal of Mammalogy,* 34:127 (1953).

Pringle, Laurence R., "Notes on Coyotes in Southern New England." *Journal of Mammalogy,* 41:278 (1960).

Robinson, Weldon B., and Cummings, Maynard W., "Notes on Behavior of Coyotes." *Journal of Mammalogy,* 28:63 (1947).

Schwartz, Charles W. and Elizabeth R., *The Wild Mammals of Missouri.* Columbia, University of Missouri Press and Missouri Conservation Commission, 1959.

Seton, Ernest Thompson, *Lives of Game Animals.* Boston, Charles T. Branford Company, 1909.

Seton, Ernest Thompson, *Life Histories of Northern Animals.* New York, Charles Scribner's Sons, 1909.

Silver, Helenette, *A History of New Hampshire Game and Furbearers.* Concord, New Hampshire Fish and Game Department, 1957.

Skinner, M. P., "The Pronghorn." *Journal of Mammalogy,* 3:102 (1922).

Sooter, Clarence A., "Speed of Predator and Prey." *Journal of Mammalogy,* 24:102 (1943).

Sperry, Charles C., "Food Habits of Peg-Leg Coyotes." *Journal of Mammalogy,* 20:190 (1939).

Sperry, Charles C., *Food Habits of the Coyote.* Washington, U.S. Department of the Interior, Fish and Wildlife Service, 1941.

Squire, Lorene, "Coyote of the Plains." *Nature Magazine,* Vol. 17, No. 3 (March, 1931), pp. 163–167.

Stevenson, Elmo, "The Case of Reddy—A Coyote." *Nature Magazine,* Vol. 27, No. 3 (March, 1936), pp. 140–142.

144

Bibliography

Swendsen, Dave, "Man Against Coyote." *Wisconsin Conservation Bulletin,* Vol. 28, No. 3 (May-June, 1963), pp. 20–21.

Thone, Frank, "Useful Pariah." *Science News Letter,* Vol. 55, No. 5 (January, 1949), pp. 78.

Trippensee, R. E., *Wildlife Management.* McGraw-Hill Book Company, Inc., 1953.

Warfel, H. E., "A Coyote in Hampshire County, Massachusetts." *Journal of Mammalogy,* 18:241 (1937).

Warren, Edward Royal, *The Mammals of Colorado.* Norman, University of Oklahoma Press, 1941.

Whiteman, Eldon E., "Habits and Pelage Changes in Captive Coyotes." *Journal of Mammalogy,* 21:435 (1940).

Young, Stanley P., and Jackson, Hartley H. T., *The Clever Coyote.* The Stackpole Company, Harrisburg, Pa., and The Wildlife Management Institute, Washington, D. C., 1951.

Index

147

The World of the Coyote

Index